A Review of Free Electron Lasers*

C. W. Roberson

P. Sprangle

1990

*Published in Physics of Fluids, 1, 3 (1989)

PHYS

PREFACE

Over the past decade a new source of coherent high-power radiation has been developed. This source, called the free electron laser (FEL), is unique in that the radiation is tunable over a wide range of wavelengths. The present research efforts are in fact a revival and extension of earlier work which was carried out during the fifties. In these early microwave experiments the lasing mechanism was clearly identified. With the discovery of the atomic laser and the transistor, research on coherent free electron radiation sources experienced a period of comparative neglect. In the last decade, however, advances in accelerator technology and the fabrication of high-field magnets, among other developments, have led to a resurgence of interest in free electron lasers.

The U.S. Navy has played a key role in the development of the FEL. At the Naval Research Laboratory (NRL) pioneering experiments in the early seventies, using high-current Marx-pulse line accelerators and an induction linac, were carried out. At about the same time researchers at Stanford University (using a superconducting linac funded by the Office of Naval Research (ONR)) were successful in obtaining coherent free electron radiation in the IR regime (10.6 and 3.4 μm). Significant new ideas on collective effects, nonlinear efficiency enhancement and optical guiding were initially developed at NRL. An ONR sponsored workshop which started with approximately ten participants has evolved into the International Free Electron Laser Conference, with over one hundred and eighty papers presented at the 1989 meeting. Personnel from NRL and ONR continue to be active participants in these conferences.

iii

The Strategic Defense Initiative Organization (SDIO) has chosen the FEL as the radiation source for directed energy weapons applications. The NRL theory group played a key role in the early phases of the program when critical decisions regarding source options were required. The SDIO FEL program on medical and material applications is managed by ONR. In a joint effort, NRL has teamed with the National Institute of Standards and Technology to use a Racetrack Microtron Accelerator to drive a free electron laser at wavelengths ranging from 200 nm to 10 μm. For its part, ONR has funded an infrared FEL facility at the University of California at Santa Barbara and continues to make a number of awards annually to individual investigators for free electron laser research.

The present review covers a critical period in the development of the FEL, beginning with its rediscovery by a new generation of scientists advocating new ideas and demonstrating its potential with new technologies. An attempt is made to present the ideas as clearly as possible, discussing the key experiments, and providing a complete bibliography. Such a task is never complete, for FEL research is active and constantly changing its character.

Dr. T. Coffey
Director of Research
U.S. Naval Research Laboratory

CONTENTS

A Review of Free Electron Lasers

Free-electron laser (FEL) theory and experiments are reviewed. The physical mechanism responsible for the generation of coherent radiation in the FEL is described and the fundamental role of the ponderomotive wave in bunching and trapping the beam is emphasized. The relationship of the FEL interaction to the beam-plasma interaction is pointed out. Various FEL operating regimes are discussed; these include the high-gain Compton and Raman regimes, both with and without an axial guiding magnetic field. The linear and nonlinear regimes are examined in detail, with particular emphasis on techniques for achieving efficiency enhancement. The quality of the electron beam used to drive FELs is a critical factor in determining the gain and efficiency. The subject of electron beam quality, for different accelerators, is discussed. Key proof-of-principle experiments for FELs in an axial guiding magnetic field, as well as those driven by induction linacs, rf linacs, electrostatic accelerators and storage rings are reviewed. Finally, the requirements on wigglers and resonators are discussed.

I. INTRODUCTION

The free-electron laser (FEL) is a classical device that uses a beam of electrons passing through a transverse periodic magnetic field to amplify electromagnetic radiation. It is a tunable, efficient, radiation source that is driven by electron beams with energies ranging from hundreds of kilovolts to hundreds of megavolts. Since the radiation wavelength varies with electron energy, it can be continuously tuned in frequency. In addition, it does not require a slow wave structure

1

and hence can be operated at short wavelengths and high power levels. The FEL has thus become the conceptual alternative to most radiation sources at wavelengths ranging from the soft x ray to the microwave regime.[1-4] Some of the present and future areas of FEL applications include sources for advanced accelerators, advanced radars, heating of fusion plasmas, medical and materials research, and directed energy applications. In this paper we review FEL theory and experiments.

Langmuir's invention of the vacuum diffusion pump and discovery of the oxide cathode, when combined with DeForest's control grid, formed the foundations of the electronics industry. Two of the most critical technologies developed during World War II were radar and the proximity fuse. Both of these devices relied on the generation of coherent electromagnetic radiation from free-electron sources. The research on short wavelength radiation was dominated by quantum electronics after the invention of the maser and laser in the late 1950s. Research in controlled magnetic fusion during the 1960s created interest in beam–plasma interactions and other plasma instabilities. The collective particle dynamics of some of the plasma instabilities is similar to those encountered in free-electron radiation sources.

Figure 1 is a plot of the power versus wavelength of high power coherent radiation sources such as FEL's, gyrotrons, and conventional microwave tubes. The potential FEL operating range not only covers the entire wavelength spectrum, but maximum power levels are comparable with other conventional high power coherent sources.

In 1951 Motz showed analytically that radiation could be amplified on an electron beam propagating through a magnetic undulator.[5,6] The amplification process that he described was the theoretical basis for the FEL mechanism.

2

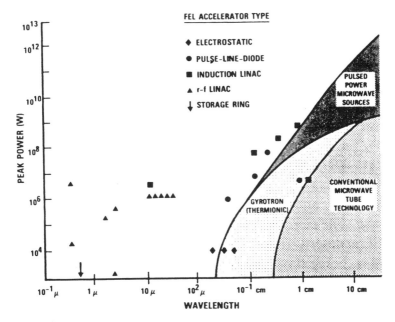

Fig. 1 — Power vs wavelength for some typical high power coherent radiation sources are shown. The output from FEL sources is shown together with the type of electron accelerator. The visible FEL's utilizing storage ring electron beams, are at a power level below the scale of the graph.

Phillips first demonstrated in 1960 the capability of a micro-wave source based on this mechanism.[7,8] His device was called the ubitron. Interest in FEL's was rekindled when Madey and co-workers built and operated a FEL device at infrared wavelengths in the late 1970s.[9-11]

In this paper the relationship of the FEL to other micro-wave devices and plasma physics will be emphasized. In particular, the similarities between FEL physics and the physics of beam–plasma interactions will be highlighted. The linear theory of the beam–plasma instability was extensively studied theoretically and summarized by Briggs.[12] The quasilin-

3

ear theory of the warm beam–plasma instability was developed by Drummond and Pines[13] and Vedenov *et al.*[14] The nonlinear saturation mechanism of the cold beam–plasma instability was proposed by Drummond *et al.*[15] and detailed theoretical calculations carried out by O'Neil *et al.*[16] and Thompson.[17] This instability served as a model for the development of large scale computer simulations by Dawson and Shanny[18] and Morse and Nielsen.[19] A detailed experimental test of quasilinear theory was carried out by Roberson *et al.*[20,21] Gentle *et al.*[22,23] demonstrated that the nonlinear saturation of the cold beam–plasma instability was caused by the trapping of electrons in the fastest growing wave. Intense relativistic electron beams have also been proposed for heating plasmas to thermonuclear temperatures.[24]

The 1970s saw a revival of interest in electron-beam-driven coherent radiation sources. The ubitron, later called the free-electron laser, evolved as the extension of traveling wave tubes.[25,26] The development of high current Marx pulse-line electron accelerators made possible the generation of very high peak power millimeter waves.[27,28]

The 1980s saw a number of proof-of-principle FEL experiments using a variety of electron accelerators. Many of these experiments will be reviewed in this paper.

Free-electron laser research has stimulated a number of new ideas. In 1971 Madey published a quantum mechanical analysis of a low current relativistic electron beam passing through a periodic magnetic field.[9] In 1974 Sprangle[29] carried out an analysis of the ubitron that included collective effects, and obtained the growth rates in the collective (Raman) operating regime for a FEL immersed in an axial guide magnetic field.[30] Colson[31] showed in 1977 that the low-gain Compton regime could be treated as a dynamical problem which could be modeled with a pendulum equation. The pendulum equation was also derived and analyzed by Kolomenskii and Lebedev.[32] The possibility of recirculating the electron beam through the wiggler to improve overall efficiency was also considered by these authors.[32] Kroll and McMullin[33] found the growth rates in the high-gain Compton regime in 1978. In 1979 Madey[34] published a theorem relating the small-signal gain to the spontaneous power spectrum in the low-gain Compton regime. Growth rates and saturation levels of all the FEL operating regimes were derived in Refs. 35–37 and will be discussed in Sec. II.

The nonlinear saturation in traveling wave amplifiers[38] and beam–plasma instabilities[15] is due to particle trapping of the beam by the space-charge wave. Early work by Phillips suggested that the efficiency in ubitrons could be improved by tapering the wiggler after particle trapping occurred.[7,8] In 1979 Sprangle et al.[39,40] showed, using a fully nonlinear formulation of the FEL, that efficiency enhancements of well over an order of magnitude could be achieved by spatially varying (decreasing) the wiggler period. Tapering the wiggler period in this way decreases the phase velocity of the ponderomotive wave and maintains trapping of the beam electrons. Using a computer simulation code Lin and Dawson[41] showed that modest increases in efficiency could be achieved by temporally increasing the wiggler amplitude. Increasing the magnetic wiggler amplitude, however, results in electron detrapping from the ponderomotive wave, making this enhancement method less attractive. An alternative approach to efficiency enhancement is to fix the magnetic wiggler period while decreasing the magnetic wiggler amplitude.[42,43] These efficiency enhancement techniques were subsequently considered by a number of other authors.[44–46]

Most of these methods assume that saturation in the linear regime takes place when the beam particles are trapped in the ponderomotive potential well of the wave. Efficiency enhancement can be accomplished by tapering either the wiggler period or the wiggler amplitude. An alternative technique is to apply a dc electric field after the beam has been trapped in the ponderomotive wave.[47,48] This technique was first used for the two-stream instability by Morales[49] and demonstrated in a traveling wave tube by Tsunoda and Malmberg.[50] A nonlinear efficiency enhancement technique that does not rely on trapping of the beam particles but depends instead on varying the phase velocity of the ponderomotive wave to pass through the beam has been proposed by Kroll et al.[43] and further developed by Rosenbluth et al.[51] This technique can be effective in cyclic devices such as storage rings where the beam becomes thermalized after passing through the wiggler. The primary emphasis of the analytical treatment in this paper will be on the FEL operating regimes in which the gain is exponential, rather than the low-gain Compton regime[31,37,52] where typically collective effects are not important.

To understand the origin and the central role played by the ponderomotive force in bunching the beam electrons we consider a low current electron beam in which the space-charge forces can be neglected. We then examine how the various components of the fields and beam velocities combine to produce the ponderomotive force that bunches the electrons in the axial direction.

In Secs. II and III, a physical model that consists of a relativistic electron beam of arbitrary intensity entering and propagating through a static helically polarized wiggler field is adopted. This one-dimensional model is sufficient to demonstrate the principal features of the self-consistent interac-

6

tion of the radiation field with the beam particles. The linear theory presented in Sec. II and the nonlinear theory in Sec. III follow the work of Sprangle et al.[37,40,53]

We have chosen a one-dimensional model to emphasize the dynamics of the interaction between the pondero-motive/space-charge waves with the beam particles. However, a three-dimensional model is required to include effects due to the transverse and axial spatial variations of the wiggler and the optical fields. In addition to the rapid wiggle motion, electrons undergo slow betatron oscillations in the transverse plane because of wiggler field gradients. Under certain conditions, the radiation field may self-focus on the electron beam. This important effect, referred to as optical guiding, was first analyzed in a three-dimensional model by Sprangle and Tang in 1981[54] in the low-gain Compton regime, and by Kroll et al.[43] and Prosnitz et al.[45] in one-dimensional analyses. Optical guiding has also been investigated by Moore,[55] Scharlemann et al.,[56] and Sprangle et al.[57] in the high-gain Compton regime. Optical guiding becomes a critical factor in extending the FEL interaction distance. The three-dimensional FEL theory is presented in Sec. IV.

Colson et al.[58,59] have pointed out the existence of higher harmonics in the emission spectrum of a FEL. This can significantly extend the tunable range of the FEL to shorter wavelengths. Coherent harmonic generation is important because of possible applications and also because of mirror damage from the harmonics in the UV region and beyond. Harmonics have been observed on the Mark III FEL at Stanford University.[60] Experiments at the National Bureau of Standards (NBS) using a microtron accelerator are specifically designed to study harmonic generation.[61]

Free-electron lasers are susceptible to the growth of sideband frequencies. This leads to the spatial and temporal

7

modulation of the output signal and an increase in spectral width. The excitation of sidebands is due to the coupling of the main signal and parasitic frequencies via the synchrotron oscillatory motion of the electrons in the ponderomotive potential wave. This instability was first studied in the FEL by Kroll *et al.*,[43,62] and further analyzed by a number of other researchers.[63-69] Sidebands have been observed in FEL experiments at Columbia University[70-72] and Los Alamos National Laboratory (LANL).[73,74] The excitation of sidebands in nonlinear wave–particle interaction was observed in early beam–plasma experiments performed by Wharton *et al.*[75] This instability has been investigated extensively both experimentally[76-78] and theoretically.[79-81]

A number of schemes have been proposed to suppress the growth of sideband frequencies in FEL oscillators. One approach is to detune the cavity away from the peak of the gain spectrum[74] by varying the mirror separation. Another technique involves the use of multilayer dielectric mirrors with wavelength-dependent reflectivity to discriminate against the most intense sidebands.[67] Experiments at Columbia University indicate reduced sideband growth in a tapered wiggler.[72] This appears to be consistent with simulations by Hafizi *et al.*,[68] which indicate a decrease in the rate of sideband growth as the rate of wiggler tapering is increased.

The FEL laser in an axial guide magnetic field is treated in Sec. V. Axial guide fields are usually employed to balance space-charge forces in high current (1 kA), low voltage (1 MeV) electron beams. However, the axial magnetic field also introduces the possibility of gain enhancement near cyclotron resonance[30,82-84] and the potential for generating very high currents and high beam quality.[85]

8

Electron beam quality, which is discussed in Sec. VI, is the critical factor in scaling the FEL to shorter wavelengths and higher power levels. The FEL voltage requirements are well within the range of existing accelerator technology. However, both the growth rate and efficiency strongly depend on the current and beam energy spread. Although the FEL does not require a waveguide (which is a limitation on the electron beam power at short wavelengths in conventional microwave tubes), a small beam size is desirable for matching to the waist of the radiation beam. This places a requirement on the beam emittance, or transverse energy spread of the beam. The electron beam brightness, which is a measure of the transverse phase space density of the beam, is often taken as a figure of merit for electron beams. An alternative figure of merit for electron beams driving FEL's is the ratio of the current density to the relative axial energy spread.[85] The beam–plasma instability changes from a fluid to a kinetic interaction as the beam density and/or temperature are increased.[21,86] The interaction can be characterized in terms of the scaled thermal velocity, which is a function of density and temperature. A similar parametrization can be made for the FEL interaction.[87] The accelerator requirements for FEL's have been reviewed by Saxon,[88] Cooper et al.,[89] Briggs et al.,[90] and Penner.[91]

The discussion of FEL experiments in Sec. VII is divided into five subsections: A. Free-electron lasers in an axial guiding magnetic field, B. Free-electron lasers driven by induction linacs, C. Free-electron lasers driven by rf linacs, D. Free-electron lasers driven by electrostatic accelerators, and E. Free-electron lasers driven by storage rings.

Some of the key FEL experiments in an axial magnetic field will be discussed in detail. A high power 35 MW, 4 mm experiment at the Naval Research Laboratory (NRL)[92] made power measurements as a function of axial magnetic field. Columbia University has carried out the difficult task of measuring the beam quality by Thomson scattering[93] and nonlinear experiments on efficiency enhancement, sidebands,[71] and optical guiding.[94] At the Massachusetts Institute of Technology (MIT) detailed experiments and comparisons with theory using a low voltage (175 kV), low current (1–8 A) electron beam have been performed.[95] The gain as a function of wiggler field was measured and shown to be in good agreement with computer simulations. The frequency-voltage characteristics were measured near resonance. Free-electron laser experiments on the two microsecond induction linac at NRL are reviewed.[96,97] In these experiments, the beam transport from a field-free region into a field-immersed wiggler were examined. Without the guide field, powers in excess of 1 MW at 30 GHz were measured. The experimental test accelerator (ETA) induction linac FEL experiments at Lawrence Livermore National Laboratory (LLNL) have produced gigawatt powers at 35 GHz by tapering the wiggler amplitude.[98,99] The first FEL experiments to be carried out at infrared wavelengths were performed at Stanford University using a superconducting rf linear accelerator.[10,11] The Stanford superconducting accelerator (SCA) has produced 0.5 μm radiation by recirculating the beam to obtain 115 MeV. Optical guiding and harmonic generation experiments have been carried out on the Mark III at Stanford University.[100] The LANL FEL group[101] has carried out experiments on sidebands and frequency tuning from 9–35 mm and reported efficiencies of 4%. To date, the highest power and shortest wavelength has been reported (40 MW at 0.6 μm) from the Boeing Aerospace rf linac experiments. The electrostatic accelerator FEL experiment at the University of California at Santa Barbara (UCSB) is designed to be a computer controlled user's facility in the infrared regime. This FEL produces a very narrow line width as a result of the long pulse (5 μsec), high quality electron beam.[102] Finally, the first operation of a visible FEL was obtained using the Orsay storage ring.[103]

The substantial progress in FEL research has been made possible, in part, by developments in the design and fabrication of wigglers.[104] This subject is discussed in Sec. VIII. In oscillator experiments, most of the work has been in adapting the optical cavities used for conventional lasers to the FEL configuration.[105] Section VIII contains a brief description of this work.

Free-electron laser research has stimulated active programs in a number of countries and has been the subject of numerous international conferences[106-109] and special journal issues.[110-113]

II. LINEAR THEORY OF THE FREE-ELECTRON LASER

The essential feature of the FEL mechanism is that the beam electrons undergo axial bunching in the combined wiggler and radiation fields. It is the axial electron bunching that is responsible for the generation of coherent radiation. In this section we will discuss the details of the FEL mechanism in the linear or small-signal regime. The nonlinear dynamics will be discussed in Sec. III.

A. The ponderomotive force

To understand the origin and central role played by the ponderomotive force in bunching the electrons, let us consider a low current electron beam in which the space-charge

11

forces can be neglected. We assume that the initial velocity of the electron beam is in the axial direction and that we have a linear magnetic wiggler field polarized in the y direction; that is $\mathbf{v}_z = v_{z0}e_z$ and $B_w = B_w \sin(k_w z)\hat{e}_y$, where v_{z0} is the axial beam velocity, B_w the wiggler magnetic field, $k_w = 2\pi/\lambda_w$, and λ_w is the wiggler period.

As a result of the Lorentz force, the beam electrons will acquire a wiggle velocity in a direction perpendicular to $\mathbf{v}_z$ and B_w, which is given by $\mathbf{v}_w = v_w \cos(k_w z)\hat{e}_x$.

We now assume the presence of a linearly polarized radiation field $\mathbf{E} + \mathbf{B} = E \cos(kz - \omega t)\hat{e}_x + B \cos(kz - \omega t)\hat{e}_y$ where $k = \omega/c$ is the radiation wavenumber. This radiation field can exist as part of the noise spectrum in the case of the oscillator or is supplied externally in the case of an amplifier.

As a result of the wiggler field and the radiation field, a ponderomotive force in the z direction develops, $F_z \simeq - (|e|/c)(\mathbf{v}_w \times \mathbf{B})_z$, which is proportional to $\sin[(k + k_w)z - \omega t]$. For relativistic beams, the ponderomotive force in the z direction arises primarily from the interaction between $\mathbf{v}_w$ and the magnetic component of the radiation field. This ponderomotive force drives a longitudinal current density δJ_z and in turn a density modulation δn that are related by $|e|\partial\delta n/\partial t = - \nabla\cdot\delta J_z\hat{e}_z$. Note that the density modulation on the electron beam, driven by the ponderomotive force, is proportional to $\cos[(k + k_w)z - \omega t]$. The density modulation on the electron beam results in a transverse current that can drive radiation that is in phase with the original radiation field. The transverse current density has the form $\delta \mathbf{J} = - |e|\delta n\mathbf{v}_w \cos(kz - \omega t)\hat{e}_x$. That is, the perturbed beam density coupled with the wiggler velocity generates a transverse component of current with a wavenumber and frequency equal to that of the original radiation field. This component of the perturbed current density is a source of coherent radiation that is in phase with the existing radiation. This process is illustrated in Fig. 2, where the electron beam is shown entering the wiggler, acquiring a component of velocity in the direction perpendicular to the wiggler field, and being modulated by the ponderomotive force.

If the ponderomotive force drives the density modulation $\delta n[(k+k_w),\omega]$ at a frequency and wavenumber nearly equal to the frequency and wavenumber of the beam space-charge mode, then the FEL is said to operate in the collective regime. In this case the ponderomotive force is very effective in modulating the beam.

To determine the radiation wavelength, we note that the interaction is strongest when the phase velocity of the ponderomotive wave is near the axial beam velocity, $v_{\mathrm{ph}} = \omega/(k+k_w) \simeq v_{z0}$. Taking $\omega = ck$ for the radiation, the output wavelength becomes

$$\lambda = \lambda_w (1-\beta_{z0})/\beta_{z0} \simeq \lambda_w/2\gamma_z^2,$$

where $\beta_{z0} = v_{z0}/c$ and $\gamma_z = (1-\beta_{z0}^2)^{-1/2}$. This is the well-known wavelength scaling relation that allows the FEL to be a tunable source of radiation. [In terms of the total γ_0 this can be written as $\lambda = \lambda_w (1+a_w^2/2)/2\gamma_0^2$, where $a_w = |e|B_w\lambda_w/2\pi m_0 c^2$ is called the wiggler constant.]

B. The free-electron laser interaction

The physical model consists of a relativistic electron beam of arbitrary intensity entering and propagating through a static helically polarized wiggler field.[53] Only spatial variations along the z axis will be considered for the electron beam, wiggler field, radiation fields, and space-charge waves. In both the linear[53] and nonlinear analysis[40] contained in this paper, a helically polarized wiggler field is used. Using our model we obtain expressions for the radiation field, the perturbed charge density, and ponderomotive potential. This set of coupled equations fully describes the FEL interaction. A dispersion relation, in the high-gain regimes, is derived, which shows explicitly the coupling of the electromagnetic and space-charge waves by the wiggler field.

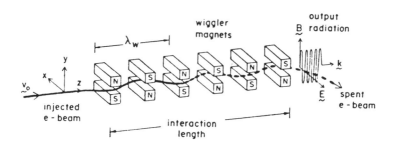

Fig. 2 — Shows a typical FEL amplifier configuration employing a linearly polarized wiggler field

For cold electron beams, we find two regimes where the radiation grows exponentially. In the Raman regime, the contribution to the perturbed beam density (and hence radiation output) due to the self-consistent space-charge potential is greater than that due to the ponderomotive potential. In the high-gain Compton regime the contribution to the perturbed beam density from the ponderomotive wave dominates that due to the self-consistent space-charge potential.

We also obtain the small-signal radiation gain with space-charge effects in the low-gain Compton regime. This result is obtained by taking Laplace transforms of the three

equations for the ponderomotive potential, density perturbation, and radiation field. The low-gain Compton mechanism is a result of constructive interference of modes rather
than exponential growth of an instability, as is the case in the
Raman and high-gain Compton regimes.

The helically polarized, static, periodic, magnetic
wiggler is taken to have the form

$$\mathbf{B}_w(z) = B_w [\cos(k_w z)\hat{e}_x + \sin(k_w z)\hat{e}_y], \tag{1}$$

where B_w is constant, $k_w = 2\pi/\lambda_w$, and λ_w is the wiggler
wavelength. This form is sufficient for particles near the axis,
i.e., $k_w r_b \ll 1$ where r_b is the beam radius. A more realistic
representation can be found in the work of Diament.[114] The
vector potential associated with this wiggler field is

$$\mathbf{A}_w = A_w (e^{ik_w z}\hat{e}_- + e^{-ik_w z}\hat{e}_+), \tag{2}$$

where $A_w = B_w/k_w$ and $\hat{e}_\pm = (\hat{e}_x \pm i\hat{e}_y)/2$. Electrons
streaming axially in the presence of the wiggler field (2) and
radiation field produce a driving current that can stimulate
(amplify) the imposed radiation field. The radiation field,
which we will represent by its vector potential $A_R(z,t)$,
evolves according to the wave equation

$$\left(\frac{\partial^2}{\partial z^2} - \frac{1}{c^2}\frac{\partial^2}{\partial t^2}\right)\mathbf{A}_R = -\frac{4\pi}{c}F\mathbf{J}_\perp, \tag{3}$$

where $J_\perp$ is the ponderomotive induced transverse driving
current, $F = \sigma_b/\sigma_R$ is the filling factor associated with the
radiation field, and σ_b and σ_R are the cross-sectional areas of
the electron beam and radiation beam, respectively. In a
form similar to the representation of the wiggler field (2) we
represent the stimulated radiation by

$$\mathbf{A}_R(z,t) = A_R (e^{i\phi(z,t)}\hat{e}_+ + e^{-i\phi(z,t)}\hat{e}_-), \tag{4}$$

where A_R is the amplitude, $\phi(z,t) = kz - \omega t$ is the phase, k is the complex wavenumber, and ω is the real frequency. The wiggler induced transverse driving current is given by

$$J_\perp(z,t) = -|e|(\delta n \mathbf{v}_w + n_0 \mathbf{v}_R) + (\text{nonresonant terms}),$$

(5)

where δ_n is the perturbed beam density, $\mathbf{v}_w$ is the transverse velocity induced by the wiggler field, n_0 is the ambient beam density, and $\mathbf{v}_R$ is the transverse velocity induced by the radiation electric field. The transverse wiggle and radiation velocities are obtained from the relativistic force equation for the particles

$$\frac{d\mathbf{P}}{dt} = -|e|\left(\mathbf{E} + \frac{\mathbf{P} \times \mathbf{B}}{\gamma m_0 c}\right),$$

(6)

where $\mathbf{P} = \gamma m_0 \mathbf{v}$ and $\gamma = (1 + \mathbf{P} \cdot \mathbf{P}/m_0 c^2)^{1/2} = (1 - \mathbf{v} \cdot \mathbf{v}/c^2)^{-1/2}$ is the total relativistic mass factor. The fields $\mathbf{E}$ and $\mathbf{B}$ are

$$\mathbf{E}(z,t) = -\frac{\partial \Phi}{\partial z}\hat{e}_z - \frac{1}{c}\frac{\partial \mathbf{A}_R}{\partial t},$$

(7a)

$$\mathbf{B}(z,t) = \frac{\partial}{\partial z}[\hat{e}_z \times (\mathbf{A}_w + \mathbf{A}_R)],$$

(7b)

where Φ is the space-charge potential associated with the perturbed density δn, and is given by

$$\frac{\partial^2 \Phi}{\partial z^2} = 4\pi|e|\delta n.$$

(7c)

Note that (7c) should contain a filling factor associated with the space-charge field. This filling factor has been set equal to unity since it is assumed that the space-charge fields fall off rapidly away from the electron beam, i.e., the radiation wavelength is small compared to the electron beam radius.

From (6), conservation of canonical transverse momentum, i.e., $\gamma m_0 v - |e|(\mathbf{A}_w + \mathbf{A}_R)/c = \text{const}$, implies that

$$\mathbf{v}_w = (|e|/\gamma_0 m_0 c)\mathbf{A}_w \qquad (8a)$$

and

$$\mathbf{v}_R = (|e|/\gamma_0 m_0 c)\mathbf{A}_R. \qquad (8b)$$

Note that since $|A_w| \gg |A_R|$ we have replaced γ with γ_0, where

$$\gamma_0 = \gamma_z [1 + (|e|A_w/m_0 c^2)^2]^{1/2}$$

and

$$\gamma_z = (1 - v_{z0}^2/c^2)^{-1/2}.$$

Substituting (5) together with (8) into (3) yields

$$\left(\frac{\partial^2}{\partial z^2} - \frac{1}{c^2}\frac{\partial^2}{\partial t^2} - F\frac{\omega_b^2}{\gamma_0 c^2}\right)\mathbf{A}_R = \frac{4\pi|e|^2\delta n}{\gamma_0 m_0 c^2}F\mathbf{A}_w, \qquad (9)$$

where $\omega_b = (4\pi|e|^2 n_0/m_0)^{1/2}$ is the beam–plasma frequency. From Eq. (9) we see that the radiation field, $\mathbf{A}_R$, is driven by the wiggler field $\mathbf{A}_w$ and the beam density perturbation δn. The perturbed beam density must now be determined self-consistently, in terms of the radiation and wiggler fields. From charge conservation, the perturbed beam density is given by

$$\frac{\partial \delta n}{\partial t} = \frac{1}{|e|}\frac{\partial \delta J_z}{\partial z}, \qquad (10)$$

where δJ_z is the perturbed axial beam current given by

$$\delta J_z(z,t) = -|e|(n_0\delta v_z + \delta n v_{z0}). \qquad (11)$$

In Eq. (11), δv_z and v_{z0} are the perturbed and unperturbed axial electron velocities. Combining (10) and (11) yields the following expression for the perturbed density:

$$\frac{d\delta n}{dt} = -n_0\frac{\partial\delta v_z}{\partial z}. \tag{12}$$

Taking the axial component of the force equation, Eq. (6), and using the relation $d\gamma/dt = -|e|(\mathbf{v}\cdot\mathbf{E})/m_0 c^2$, we find that

$$\frac{dv_z}{dt} = -\frac{|e|}{\gamma_0 m_0}\left(-\frac{\partial\Phi}{\partial z} + c^{-1}(\mathbf{v}\times\mathbf{B})\cdot\hat{e}_z - c^{-2}(\mathbf{v}\cdot\mathbf{E})\right). \tag{13}$$

Linearizing (13) by keeping terms to first order in the radiation field yields

$$\frac{d\delta v_z}{dt} = \frac{|e|}{\gamma_0 m_0}\left[\gamma_z^{-2}\frac{\partial\Phi(z,t)}{\partial z} + \left(\frac{\partial}{\partial z} + c^{-2}v_{z0}\frac{\partial}{\partial t}\right)\Phi_p(z,t)\right]. \tag{14}$$

In Eq. (14), the γ_z^{-2} relativistic reduction in the space-charge field comes from combining the terms $\partial\Phi/\partial z$ and $-(v_{z0}/c)^2\,\partial\Phi/\partial z$ in Eq. (13). The axial force terms, $\mathbf{v}\times\mathbf{B}/c$ and $v_{z0}(v_\perp\cdot E_\perp)/c^2$, can be written in terms of an effective potential called the ponderomotive potential Φ_p, where

$$\Phi_p(z,t) = -|e|\mathbf{A}_w\cdot\mathbf{A}_R/\gamma_0 m_0 c^2$$

$$= (-|e|A_w A_R/2\gamma_0 m_0 c^2)e^{i[(k+k_w)z-\omega t]} + \text{c.c.} \tag{15}$$

We see from Eq. (14) that the beam velocity and hence density is driven by both the ponderomotive and space-charge potential waves. The ponderomotive wave in turn is proportional to the product of the wiggler and radiation field amplitudes. Taking the convective time derivative of both sides of (12) and employing (14) yields

18

$$\frac{d^2\delta n}{dt^2} = \frac{-|e|n_0}{\gamma_0 m_0}\left[\gamma_z^{2}\frac{\partial^2\Phi(z,t)}{\partial z^2}\right.$$

$$\left.+\frac{\partial}{\partial z}\left(\frac{\partial}{\partial z}+c^{-2}v_{z0}\frac{\partial}{\partial t}\right)\Phi_p(z,t)\right]. \qquad (16)$$

Substituting (7c) into (16) and using $\partial^2\Phi/\partial z^2 = 4\pi|e|\delta n$, we obtain

$$\frac{d^2\delta n}{dt^2}+\frac{\omega_b^2}{\gamma_0\gamma_z^2}\delta n$$

$$=\frac{-|e|n_0}{\gamma_0 m_0}\frac{\partial}{\partial z}\left(\frac{\partial}{\partial z}+c^{-2}v_{z0}\frac{\partial}{\partial t}\right)\Phi_p(z,t). \qquad (17)$$

Equation (17) shows that the perturbed charge density is driven by the ponderomotive potential wave. Equations (9) and (17) together with (15) form a set of coupled relations for the radiation field and perturbed charge density. The beam density perturbation is driven by the ponderomotive wave, which is proportional to the radiation field. The radiation field in turn is driven by both the ponderomotive wave and wiggler field. The coupling in these equations, under appropriate conditions, can lead to the growth of coherent radiation.

C. FEL dispersion relation

Since the phase of the ponderomotive wave is $[(k+k_w)z-\omega t]$, we see from Eq. (17) that the perturbed density should have a similar dependence in the time asymptotic limit, hence we write

$$\delta n(z,t)=\delta\tilde{n}(k,\omega)e^{i[(k+k_w)z-\omega t]}+\text{c.c.} \qquad (18)$$

19

Using (18) together with (15), Eq. (17) becomes

$$\{[\omega - v_{z0}(k + k_w)]^2 - \omega_b^2/(\gamma_0\gamma_z^2)\}\delta\tilde{n}$$

$$= \frac{\omega_b^2}{8\pi\gamma_0^2} \frac{A_w A_R}{m_0 c^2}(k + k_w)\left(k + k_w - \frac{\omega v_{z0}}{c}\right). \qquad (19)$$

Equations (9) and (17) can be used in the high-gain regime to obtain a dispersion relation for the radiation field. In this section transient terms associated with the initial value solution of (9) and (19) will be neglected.

Substituting (18), together with the representations for A_w and $A(z,t)$ given in (2) and (4), into (9) gives

$$\left(k^2 - \frac{\omega^2}{c^2} + F\frac{\omega_b^2}{\gamma_0 c^2}\right)A_R = \frac{-4\pi|e|^2}{\gamma_0 m_0 c^2}\delta\tilde{n}FA_w. \qquad (20)$$

Eliminating $\delta\tilde{n}$ and $\tilde{A}_R$ from (19) and (20) yields the following dispersion relation:

$$(\omega^2 - c^2 k^2 - F\omega_b^2/\gamma_0)\{[\omega - v_{z0}(k + k_w)]^2 - \omega_b^2/\gamma_0\gamma_z^2\}$$

$$= F(\omega_b^2/\gamma_0)\beta_w^2 c^2 k k_w, \qquad (21)$$

where $v_w = c\beta_w = |e|A_w/(\gamma_0 m_0 c)$ is the magnitude of the electron wiggle velocity. In obtaining the final dispersion relation in (21) we used the approximations $k \simeq (1 + \beta_z)$ $\times \gamma_z^2 k_w \gg k_w$ and $\omega \simeq ck$ to simplify the terms on the right-hand side of (19), i.e.,

$$(k + k_w)(k + k_w - v_{z0}\omega/c^2) \simeq 2kk_w.$$

In (21) the first term in brackets represents the uncoupled electromagnetic mode while the second bracketed term represents the two uncoupled beam space-charge modes having an effective wavenumber $k + k_w$. The wiggler field provides for the coupling between the electromagnetic and space-charge modes. Since we will be primarily concerned with the forward traveling radiation field, we can approximate the electromagnetic mode in (21) by

$$\omega^2 - c^2 k^2 - F\omega_b^2/\gamma_0 \simeq 2\omega \left[\omega - (c^2 k^2 + F\omega_b^2/\gamma_0)^{1/2}\right].$$
(22)

Using (22) the FEL dispersion relation becomes

$$\left[k - \left(\frac{\omega^2}{c^2} - F\frac{\omega_b^2}{\gamma_0 c^2} \right)^{1/2} \right] \left[\left(k + k_w - \frac{\omega}{v_{z0}} \right)^2 - \frac{\omega_b^2}{v_{z0}^2 \gamma_0 \gamma_z^2} \right]$$

$$= - F \frac{\omega_b^2/c^2}{2\gamma_0} \beta_w^2 \beta_{z0}^{-2} k_w.$$
(23)

The dispersion relation in (23) may now be recast into the form

$$(k - k_{em})(k - k_-)(k - k_+) = -\alpha^2,$$
(24)

where

$$\alpha^2 = F(\omega_b^2/c^2/2\gamma_0)\beta_w^2 \beta_{z0}^{-2} k_w$$

is the coupling coefficient,

$$k_{em} = (\omega^2 - F\omega_b^2/\gamma_0)^{1/2}/c$$
(25a)

is the electromagnetic mode wavenumber, and

$$k_\pm = \left[\omega - v_{z0}k_w \pm \omega_b/(\gamma_z\sqrt{\gamma_0}) \right]/v_{z0}$$
(25b)

is the wavenumber of the positive and negative energy beam space-charge modes, respectively. We can now distinguish two high-gain operating regimes of the FEL mechanism. These are often referred to as the high-gain Compton (strong wiggler) and Raman regimes.[33,37]

For a sufficiently thermal electron beam, the high-gain growth rate becomes proportional to the slope of the beam

21

distribution function at the phase velocity of the pondero-motive wave.[37,115]

D. High-gain Compton regime

In this regime the forces on the beam electrons due to the ponderomotive wave dominates that due to the collective space-charge effects. This can also be referred to as the strong wiggler field limit or tenuous beam limit. In this limit the dispersion relation (23) reduces to

$$(k - k_{em})[k - (\omega/v_{z0} - k_w)]^2 = -\alpha^2, \qquad (26)$$

where the space-charge term that comes about from the self-consistent scalar potential, i.e., $\omega_b/(v_{z0}\gamma_z\sqrt{\gamma_0})$ has been ne-glected. From the character of the dispersion relation in (26) it is clear that this regime involves the coupling of an electromagnetic mode with the ponderomotive wave. The maximum spatial growth rate occurs when k_{em} is equal to $(\omega - v_{z0}k_w)v_{z0}$ and is given by

$$\Gamma = \frac{\sqrt{3}}{2} F^{1/3}\left(\frac{\beta_w^2}{2} \frac{\omega_b^2 k_w}{\gamma_0 c^2}\right)^{1/3} \qquad (27)$$

In obtaining (27) we used the approximations, $\omega \simeq ck$ and $\beta_{0z} \simeq 1$. The dispersion relation in (26) was obtained by ne-glecting the space-charge term; this implies the following inequality between the wiggler field amplitude and beam density:

$$\beta_w \gg \beta_{crit} \equiv F^{-1/2}(2\omega_b c^2/v_{z0}^3 \gamma_0^{1/2} \gamma_z^2 k_w)^{1/2}. \qquad (28)$$

At the maximum growth rate the frequency of the electro-magnetic wave is $\omega = (1 + \beta_{z0})\gamma_z^2 v_{z0} k_w \simeq 2\gamma_z^2 ck_w$, where we have neglected $\omega_b/\sqrt{\gamma_0}$ compared to ω.

22

E. Raman regime

In this regime the beam–plasma frequency is sufficiently high that the coupling between the electromagnetic wave and the two beam waves, i.e., negative and positive energy modes, can be considered independently. The dispersion relation describing the interaction between the negative energy beam wave and electromagnetic wave is obtained from (24). Here, the effect of the positive energy beam mode on the coupling is weak and therefore $k - k_+$ can be replaced by $(k_- - k_+) = 2\omega_b/(\gamma_z v_{z0}\gamma_0^{1/2})$ in (24). The resulting dispersion relation is

$$(k - k_{em})(k - k_-) = -\alpha^2 \gamma_z \gamma_0^{1/2} v_{z0}/2\omega_b. \tag{29}$$

The dispersion relation is sketched in Fig. 3. The maximum Raman growth rate occurs when $k_{em} = k$ and is

$$\Gamma = \beta_w F^{1/2}(\omega_b \gamma_z k_w/4\sqrt{\gamma_0}c)^{1/2}. \tag{30}$$

The coupling with the positive energy beam wave is indeed weak, permitting the replacement of $k - k_+$ by $(k_- - k_+)$ if

$$\beta_w \ll \beta_{crit}, \tag{31}$$

where β_{crit} is defined in (28). Note that (31) is the reverse inequality needed for the high-gain Compton regime given by (28).

An equivalent way of distinguishing the Raman regime from the high-gain Compton regime is by defining a critical beam–plasma density,

$$\omega_{b,crit} = F(v_{z0}/c)^2\gamma_0^{1/2}\gamma_z^3\beta_w^2 v_{z0}k_w/2.$$

If $\omega_b \gg \omega_{b,crit}$ the FEL operates in the Raman regime while $\omega_b \ll \omega_{b,crit}$ implies the high-gain Compton regime.

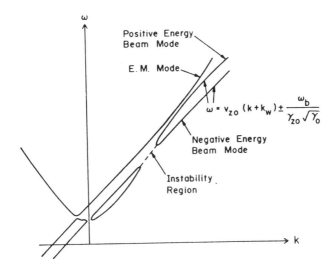

Fig. 3 — Dispersion diagram of the coupled beam space charge modes and electromagnetic mode. The Raman FEL instability occurs near the intersection between the negative energy beam mode and electromagnetic mode.

F. Low-gain Compton regime

In this section we state the results for the low-gain Compton regime of the FEL. In this limit the self-consistent space-charge potential usually plays a small role. This regime differs from the high-gain Compton regime by the role of the initial conditions. In Sec. II C we took Fourier transforms to obtain the FEL dispersion relation in (21). The Raman and high-gain Compton regimes exist in the time asymptotic limit and their characteristics are independent of the initial conditions. To obtain the gain in the low-gain Compton regime we must take Laplace transforms of Eqs. (9) and (17). In this regime, the gain with space-charge effects[116] is given by

$$G(z) = \frac{-\beta_w^2}{8} \frac{\omega_b^2}{\gamma_0 c^2} Fk_w z^3 \frac{\partial}{\partial \theta}\left[\left(1 + k_b^2 z^2 \frac{\partial^2}{\partial \theta^2}\right)\left(\frac{\sin \theta}{\theta}\right)^2\right],$$
(32)

where $k_b = (\omega_b/\gamma_{z0}c)/(24\gamma_0)^{1/2}$, $|G(z)| \ll 1$, $\theta = \Delta k z/2$, and $\Delta k = k + k_w - \omega/v_{z0}$. In the absence of space-charge effects, i.e., $k_b^2 z^2 \ll 1$, the small signal gain in (32) reduces to the usual expression.[9,31,37] Since the function $\partial(\sin \theta /\theta)^2/\partial\theta$ has a minimum value of 0.54 when $\theta = 1.3$, the maximum gain is given by

$$G(z)_{\max} \simeq (\beta_w^2 \omega_b^2/\gamma_0) Fk_w z^3,$$
(33)

where $z = 2.6/\Delta k = 2.6/(k + k_w - \omega/v_{z0})$ is the axial location of maximum gain.

G. Intrinsic efficiency in the various regimes

Estimates of the laser efficiency for monoenergetic injected electron beams can be obtained using simple trapping arguments.[37,117] In the FEL mechanism, electron trapping in the longitudinal wave, i.e., ponderomotive and space-charge wave, is the saturation mechanism when the injected electron beam is monoenergetic. The axial phase velocity of the longitudinal wave is

$$v_{ph} = \omega/[\mathrm{Re}(k) + k_w],$$
(34)

where $\mathrm{Re}(k)$ is determined from the dispersion relation. In the linear development of the laser radiation the injected axial beam velocity is slightly greater than the phase velocity, $v_{z0} = v_{ph} + \Delta v$, where $v_{ph} \gg \Delta v > 0$ and Δv depends upon the particular FEL regime under consideration. Since radiation growth occurs when $\Delta v > 0$, the phase velocity of the longitudinal wave must be slightly less than the initial axial electron velocity. The radiation amplitude increases at the expense of the electron's kinetic energy until the electrons become deeply trapped in the longitudinal wave. At this point the radiation field reaches its maximum amplitude and the average axial electron velocity is approximately given by $v_z|_{sat} = v_{ph} - \Delta v$. At saturation the average axial electron velocity has decreased by approximately $2\Delta v$. The decrease in the electron beam energy can be directly equated to the increase in radiation energy. For highly relativistic electron beams the decrease in the average electron kinetic energy is $\Delta\epsilon = 2\gamma_0\gamma_z^2 m_0 v_{z0}\Delta v$ and hence the radiation efficiency is

$$\eta = \Delta\epsilon/(\gamma_0 - 1)m_0 c^2 \simeq 2\gamma_z^2 \Delta v/c. \tag{35}$$

The longitudinal waves "see" the beam as monoenergetic if the beam's axial velocity spread is small compared to Δv. Since the fractional beam's axial energy spread is $E_{th}/E_0 = \gamma_z^2 v_{th}/c$, the monoenergetic beam approximation requires that

$$E_{th}/E_0 \ll \eta. \tag{36}$$

To obtain the intrinsic efficiency η at the maximum growth rate in the high-gain Compton regime, we first solve (26) for $\mathrm{Re}(k)$, giving

$$\mathrm{Re}(k) = \omega/v_{z0} - k_w + 2^{-4/3}F^{1/3}(\omega_b\beta_w/\sqrt{\gamma_0}ck_w)^{2/3}k_w. \tag{37}$$

Using (37) to solve for $\Delta v = v_{z0} - v_{ph}$, Eq. (35) yields the following expression for the intrinsic efficiency in the high-gain Compton regime:

$$\eta = F^{1/3}(\omega_b\beta_w/4\sqrt{\gamma_0}ck_w)^{2/3}. \tag{38}$$

Following the same procedure, the intrinsic efficiency in the Raman regime is

$$\eta = \omega_b / \sqrt{\gamma_0 \gamma_z} \, c k_w, \tag{39}$$

and in the low-gain Compton regime is given by

$$\eta = \lambda_w / (2L) = (2N)^{-1}, \tag{40}$$

where L is the interaction length and N the number of wiggler periods. Figure 4 shows the spatial growth rate and efficiency in the high-gain regimes as a function of β_w. Table I lists the various expressions for the spatial growth rates, or gain, and the corresponding intrinsic power efficiencies for the FEL operating regimes are discussed.

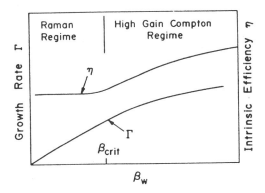

Fig. 4 — Spatial growth rate and intrinsic efficiency in the Raman and high-gain Compton regimes as a function of the normalized wiggle velocity

Operating the FEL at shorter wavelengths by increasing the beam energy or decreasing the wiggler period results in lower efficiencies and more stringent requirements on the beam energy spread. One can attempt to compensate for the

Table I — The quantities used in Table I have the following definitions: $\nu = I_b/17\beta_0 = (\omega_b r_b/2c)^2$ is Budker's parameter, I_b is the beam current in kiloamperes, L is the wiggler length, r_b is the beam radius, $\beta_w = v_w/c$, $\gamma_z = \gamma_0/(1 + \gamma_0^2\beta_w^2)^{1/2}$, $f(\theta) = \partial(\sin\theta/\theta)^2/\partial\theta$, $\theta = (1 - v_{z0}/v_{ph})\tau\omega/2$, $\tau = L/v_{z0}$ is the electron's transit time and F is the filling factor, i.e., beam area/radiation area. (c.g.s. units are used unless otherwise stated).

FEL Operating Regimes	Gain or Growth Rate	Intrinsic Power Efficiency
High-gain Compton (single-particle)	$2F^{1/3}\left[\dfrac{\nu}{\gamma_0}\right]^{1/3}\left[\dfrac{r_b}{\lambda_w}\right]^{1/3}\dfrac{\beta_w^{2/3}}{r_b}$	$0.2\,F^{1/3}\left[\dfrac{\nu}{\gamma_0}\right]^{1/3}\left[\dfrac{\lambda_w\beta_w}{r_b}\right]^{2/3}$
Raman (collective, high gain)	$(\pi\gamma_z F)^{1/2}(\nu/\gamma_0)^{1/4}\dfrac{\beta_w}{\sqrt{r_b\lambda_w}}$	$\dfrac{1}{\pi\gamma_z}\left[\dfrac{\nu}{\gamma_0}\right]^{1/2}\dfrac{\lambda_w}{r_b}$
Compton (single-particle, low-gain)	$\pi F\dfrac{\nu}{\gamma_0}\beta_w^2\dfrac{L^3}{r_b^2\lambda_w}f(\theta)$	$\dfrac{1}{2}\dfrac{\lambda_w}{L}$

low efficiency by increasing the beam current. However, this is usually associated with an increase in the effective beam energy spread.

III. NONLINEAR THEORY OF THE FREE-ELECTRON LASER

The physical model for the nonlinear analysis is identical to the one used for the linear treatment of the FEL. The wiggler field, however, is assumed to be spatially tapered,[39-43] in order to enhance efficiency.

The variable amplitude and period wiggler magnetic field can be expressed in terms of the vector potential,

$$\mathbf{A}_w(z) = A_w(z)\left[\cos\left(\int_0^z k_w(z')dz'\right)\hat{e}_x \right.$$

$$\left. + \sin\left(\int_0^z k_w(z')dz'\right)\hat{e}_y\right], \tag{41}$$

where the amplitude $A_w(z)$ and wavenumber $k_w(z)$ are known and slowly varying functions of z. The vector potential field in (41) is a good approximation to a right-handed polarized helical magnetic field near the z axis, i.e., when $k_w r_b \ll 1$, where r_b is the beam radius. The wiggler magnetic field associated with (41) is given by

$$\mathbf{B}_w(z) = B_w(z)\left[\cos\left(\int_0^z k_w(z')dz' + a(z)\right)\hat{e}_x \right.$$

$$\left. + \sin\left(\int_0^z k_w(z')dz' + a(z)\right)\hat{e}_y\right], \tag{42}$$

where $B_w(z) = -\{[k_w(z)A_w(z)]^2 + [\partial A_w(z)/\partial z]^2\}^{1/2}$, and $a(z) = -\tan^{-1}\{[\partial A_w(z)/\partial z]/[k_w(z)A_w(z)]\}$, are slowly varying functions of z. The period of the magnetic field is $\lambda_w(z) = 2\pi/[k_w(z) + \partial a/\partial z] \simeq 2\pi/k_w(z)$. The scattered electromagnetic and electrostatic fields in terms of the vector potential $\mathbf{A}_R(z,t)$ and scalar potential $\Phi(z,t)$ are taken to be of the form

$$\mathbf{A}_R(z,t) = A_R(z)[\cos\theta(z,t)\hat{e}_x - \sin\theta(z,t)\hat{e}_y], \tag{43a}$$

$$\Phi(z,t) = \Phi_1(z)\cos\theta_p(z,t) + \Phi_2(z)\sin\theta_p(z,t), \tag{43b}$$

29

where

$$\theta(z,t) = \int_0^z k(z')dz' - \omega t,$$

$$\theta_p(z,t) = \int_0^z [k(z') + k_w(z')]dz' - \omega t,$$

are the phases and the amplitudes of the potentials $A_R(z)$, $\Phi_1(z)$, and $\Phi_2(z)$ and the wavenumbers $k(z)$ and $k_w(z)$ are slowly varying functions of z. The scattered electromagnetic field represented by Eq. (43a) is a right-handed elliptically polarized field traveling in the positive z direction.

A. Wave equations

The evolution of the scattered potentials are governed by the wave equations

$$\left(\frac{\partial^2}{\partial z^2} - \frac{1}{c^2}\frac{\partial^2}{\partial t^2}\right)\mathbf{A}_R(z,t) = -\frac{4\pi}{c}F\mathbf{J}_\perp(z,t) \qquad (44a)$$

and

$$\frac{\partial^2\Phi(z,t)}{\partial z\,\partial t} = 4\pi J_z(z,t), \qquad (44b)$$

where $\mathbf{J}(z,t)$ is the driving current density. Substituting the potentials in Eqs. (43) into (44) yields

$$[\omega^2/c^2 - k^2(z)]A_R(z)\cos\theta(z,t) - 2k^{1/2}(z)$$

$$\times\frac{\partial}{\partial z}[A_R(z)k^{1/2}(z)]\sin\theta(z,t)$$

$$= -\frac{4\pi}{c}FJ_x(z,t), \qquad (45a)$$

30

$$\frac{\partial}{\partial z}[\Phi_1(z)\sin\theta_p(z,t) - \Phi_2(z)\cos\theta_p(z,t)]$$

$$= \frac{4\pi}{\omega}J_z(z,t), \tag{45b}$$

where terms proportional to $\partial^2 A_R/\partial z^2$ have been neglected. The coefficients of the sinusoidal terms on the left-hand side of Eqs. (45) are slowly varying functions of z and independent of t. The arguments of the sinusoidal terms on the other hand are rapidly varying functions of t for z fixed. The rapidly time-varying terms, for example, in Eq. (45a), can be removed by multiplying them by $\cos\theta(z,t)$, $\sin\theta(z,t)$ and taking the temporal average over one wave period, i.e., $(\omega/2\pi)\int_0^{2\pi/\omega} dt$. Performing this operation on Eq. (45a), as well as similar operations on Eq. (45b), yields

$$\left(\frac{\omega^2}{c^2} - k^2(z)\right)A_R(z) = \frac{-4\omega}{c}F\int_0^{2\pi/\omega} J_x(z,t)\cos\theta(z,t)dt, \tag{46a}$$

$$2k^{1/2}(z)\frac{\partial}{\partial z}[A_R(z)k^{1/2}(z)]$$

$$= \frac{4\omega}{c}F\int_0^{2\pi/\omega} J_x(z,t)\sin\theta(z,t)dt, \tag{46b}$$

$$[k(z) + k_w(z)]\Phi_1(z) - \frac{\partial\Phi_2(z)}{\partial z}$$

$$= 4\int_0^{2\pi/\omega} J_z(z,t)\cos\theta_p(z,t)dt, \tag{46c}$$

$$[k(z) + k_w(z)]\Phi_2(z) + \frac{\partial\Phi_1(z)}{\partial z}$$

$$= 4\int_0^{2\pi/\omega} J_z(z,t)\sin\theta_p(z,t)dt. \tag{46d}$$

31

B. Nonlinear driving currents

It is now necessary to obtain expressions for the transverse and axial components of the current densities and perform the time integration specified in Eqs. (46). In general, the nonthermal electron distribution function, written in terms of the electron orbits, is

$$f(z,\mathbf{p},t) = n_0 v_{z0} \int_{-\infty}^{t} dt_0 \, \delta[z - \tilde{z}(t_0,t)]\delta[p_x - \tilde{p}_x(t_0,t)]$$

$$\times \delta[p_y - \tilde{p}_y(t_0,t)]\delta[p_z - \tilde{p}_z(t_0,t)], \qquad (47)$$

where n_0 is the uniform particle density to the left of the interaction region, i.e., $z \leqslant 0$, v_{z0} is the constant axial electron velocity for $z \leqslant 0$, $z(t_0,t)$ is the axial position of the particle at time t that crossed the $z = 0$ plane at time t_0, and $\tilde{\mathbf{p}}(t_0,t)$ is the momentum vector of the particle at time t that crossed the $z = 0$ plane at time t_0. Thermal effects that are characteristic of actual electron beams can be easily included by appropriately modifying the electron distribution function in (47). The integral over t_0 in Eq. (47) takes into account the continuous flow of particles into the interaction region. The current density associated with this electron distribution is

$$\mathbf{J}(z,t) = \frac{-|e|n_0 v_{z0}}{m_0} \int_{-\infty}^{t} \frac{\mathbf{p}(t_0,t)\delta[t - \tau(t_0,z)]}{\gamma[\mathbf{p}(t_0,t)]|\partial \tilde{z}(t_0,t)/\partial t|} dt_0,$$

$$(48)$$

where $\gamma(\mathbf{p}) = (1 + |\mathbf{p}^2|/m_0^2 c^2)^{1/2}$ and

$$\tau(t_0,z) = t_0 + \int_0^z \frac{dz'}{v_z(t_0,z')} \qquad (49)$$

is the time it takes a particle to reach the position z if it entered the interaction region, $z = 0$, at time t_0, and $v_z(t_0,z)$

is the axial velocity of a particle at position z that was at $z = 0$ at time t_0.

The quantity $\partial \tilde{z}(t_0,t)/\partial t$ is the axial velocity v_z of a particle at time t that was at $z = 0$ at time t_0. Clearly, for $\mathbf{J}(z,t)$ to be finite, v_z should not vanish in the interaction region. We assume here that no particle is slowed down to zero velocity in the laboratory frame, hence $\gamma[\mathbf{p}(t_0,t)]m_0|\partial \tilde{z}(t_0,t)/\partial t| = p_z(t_0,t)$ and the driving current becomes

$$\mathbf{J}(z,t) = -|e|n_0 v_{z0} \int_{-\infty}^{t} \frac{\mathbf{p}(t_0,t)}{p_z(t_0,t)} \delta[t - \tau(t_0,z)]\,dt_0.$$

(50)

Substituting the above form for $\mathbf{J}(z,t)$ into the right-hand side of Eqs. (46), we obtain the self-consistent amplitudes and phases of the scattered potentials in terms of driving currents.

Since the system of particles and fields are in the temporal steady state, particles that cross the $z = 0$ plane, separated in time by $2\pi/\omega$, will execute identical orbits that are separated in time by $2\pi/\omega$. It is, therefore, possible to define a beam segment, "beamlet," for which all possible steady-state orbits of the actual beam particles are represented by the particles in the beamlet, but are displaced in time. The axial length of the beamlet is clearly $2\pi v_{z0}/\omega$. Therefore substituting (50) into (46) yields

$$\left(\frac{\omega^2}{c^2} - k^2(z)\right)A_R(z)$$

$$= 4|e|n_0\frac{v_{z0}}{c}\omega F \int_0^{2\pi/\omega} \frac{\tilde{p}_x[t_0,\tau(t_0,z)]}{\tilde{p}_z[t_0,\tau(t_0,z)]}$$

$$\times \cos\theta\,[z,\tau(t_0,z)]\,dt_0,$$

(51a)

$$2k^{1/2}(z)\frac{\partial}{\partial z}[A_R(z)k^{1/2}(z)]$$

$$= -4|e|n_0\frac{v_{z0}}{c}\omega F\int_0^{2\pi/\omega}\frac{\tilde{p}_x[t_0,\tau(t_0,z)]}{\tilde{p}_z[t_0,\tau(t_0,z)]}$$

$$\times\sin\theta\,[z,\tau(t_0,z)]dt_0, \qquad (51b)$$

$$[k(z)+k_w(z)]\Phi_1(z)-\frac{\partial\Phi(z)}{\partial z}$$

$$= -4|e|n_0v_{z0}\int_0^{2\pi/\omega}\cos\theta_p\,[z,\tau(t_0,z)]dt_0, \qquad (51c)$$

$$[k(z)+k_w(z)]\Phi_2(z)-\frac{\partial\Phi_2(z)}{\partial z}$$

$$= -4|e|n_0v_{z0}\int_0^{2\pi/\omega}\sin\theta_p\,[z,\tau(t_0,z)]dt_0. \qquad (51d)$$

Notice that on the right-hand side of the above equations the single integrals over t_0 are from 0 to $2\pi/\omega$. As we will illustrate, these integrals can be evaluated numerically by following the orbits of a relatively small number of particles that enter the interaction region in any single time interval of duration $2\pi/\omega$.

C. Particle dynamics

We now express the particle orbits, which are needed for the evaluation of Eqs. (51), in terms of the new independent variables t_0 and z. The forces exerted on the electrons arise from the wiggler and potentials given in Eqs. (41) and (43). We immediately note that the transverse canonical momenta of the particles are conserved. Therefore if both the wiggler and scattered fields are zero as $z\to-\infty$, the transverse particle momenta are given by

$$p_x(z,t) = (|e|/c)[\mathbf{A}_w(z) + \mathbf{A}_R(z,t)] \cdot \hat{e}_x \qquad (52a)$$

and

$$p_y(z,t) = (|e|/c)[\mathbf{A}_w(z) + \mathbf{A}_R(z,t)] \cdot \hat{e}_y. \qquad (52b)$$

Using Eqs. (52) the longitudinal component of the force equation can be put into the form

$$\frac{dp_z(z,t)}{dt} = \frac{-|e|^2}{2\gamma(z,t)m_0c^2}\left(\frac{\partial}{\partial z}[\mathbf{A}_w(z) + \mathbf{A}_R(z,t)]^2 \right.$$

$$\left. - 2\gamma(z,t)\frac{m_0c^2}{|e|}\frac{\partial}{\partial z}\Phi(z,t)\right), \qquad (53)$$

where $pz(z,t)$ is the axial momentum, and the relativistic mass factor is

$$\gamma(z,t) = \{1 + (|e|^2/m_0^2c^4)[\mathbf{A}_w(z) + \mathbf{A}_R(z,t)]^2$$

$$+ p_z^2(z,t)/m_0^2c^2\}^{1/2}. \qquad (54)$$

Equations (52)–(54) specify the particle dynamics in terms of the wiggler and scattered fields. The transverse and longitudinal particle motion is decoupled. Writing Eqs. (52) and (53) in terms of the new independent variables z and t_0, we find that

$$p_x(z,\tau) = (|e|/c)[A_{wx}(z) + A_{Rx}(z,\tau)], \qquad (55a)$$

$$p_y(z,\tau) = (|e|/c)[A_{wy}(z) + A_{Ry}(z,\tau)], \qquad (55b)$$

$$\frac{dp_z(z,\tau)}{dz} = -\frac{|e|^2}{2c^2p_z(z,\tau)}\left(\frac{\partial}{\partial z}|\mathbf{A}_w(z) + \mathbf{A}_R(z,\tau)|^2 \right.$$

$$\left. - 2\gamma(z,\tau)\frac{m_0c^2}{|e|}\frac{\partial}{\partial z}\Phi(z,\tau)\right). \qquad (55c)$$

35

We have expressed the particle orbits in terms of the entry time t_0 and axial position z. Note that our definition of the momenta implies that $\tilde{p}_x(t_0,\tau) = p_x(z,\tau)$, $\tilde{p}_y(t_0,\tau) = p_y(z,\tau)$, and $\tilde{p}_z(t_0,\tau) = p_z(z,\tau)$. To obtain the final set of equations for the amplitude $A_R(z)$ and wavenumber $k(z)$ we first combine Eqs. (51a) and (51b) with Eqs. (51c) and (51d), respectively. Using the expressions for $\tilde{p}_x$ and $\tilde{p}_y$ given by Eqs. (55a) and (55b), we arrive at the following expressions:

$$\left(\frac{\omega^2}{c^2} - k^2(z)\right)A_R(z)$$

$$= \frac{\omega_b^2}{2c^2}m_0 v_{z0}\frac{\omega}{\pi}F\int_0^{2\pi/\omega} \tilde{p}_z^{-1}[t_0,\tau(t_0,z)]$$

$$\times \{A_w(z)\cos\{\theta_p[z,\tau(t_0,z)]\} + A_R(z)\}dt_0, \qquad (56a)$$

$$2k^{1/2}(z)\frac{\partial}{\partial z}[A_R(z)k^{1/2}(z)]$$

$$= -\frac{\omega_b^2}{2c^2}m_0 v_{z0}\frac{\omega}{\pi}F\int_0^{2\pi/\omega} \tilde{p}_z^{-1}[t_0,\tau(t_0,z)]$$

$$\times \{A_w(z)\sin\{\theta_p[z,\tau(t_0,z)]\}\}dt_0, \qquad (56b)$$

where we have used Eqs. (41) and (43a) for $A_w(z)$ and $A_R(z,t)$ and $\omega_b = (4\pi|e|^2 n_0/m_0)^{1/2}$. For completeness we rewrite Eqs. (51c) and (51d) for the scalar space-charge potential,

$$[k(z) + k_w(z)]\Phi_1(z) - \frac{\partial\Phi_2(z)}{\partial z}$$

$$= \frac{-\omega_b^2}{c^2}\frac{v_{z0}}{\pi}\frac{m_0 c^2}{|e|}\int_0^{2\pi/\omega} \cos\{\theta_p[z,\tau(t_0,z)]\}dt_0, \qquad (57a)$$

$$[k(z) + k_w(z)]\Phi_2(z) + \frac{\partial \Phi_1(z)}{\partial z}$$

$$= \frac{-\omega_b^2}{c^2} \frac{v_{z0}}{\pi} \frac{m_0 c^2}{|e|} \int_0^{2\pi/\omega} \sin\{\theta_p[z,\tau(t_0,z)]\}dt_0. \quad (57\text{b})$$

The relevant particle dynamics is contained in Eq. (55b), which is rewritten in the form

$$\frac{d\tilde{p}_z(t_0,\tau)}{dz} = \frac{-|e|^2}{2c^2 \tilde{p}_z(t_0\tau)} \left(\frac{\partial}{\partial z} [\mathbf{A}_w(z) + \mathbf{A}_R(z,\tau)]^2 \right.$$

$$\left. - 2\gamma(z,\tau) \frac{m_0^2 c}{|e|} \frac{\partial \Phi(z,\tau)}{\partial z} \right), \quad (58)$$

where

$$\gamma(z,\tau) = \{1 + (|e|^2/m_0^2 c^4)|\mathbf{A}_w(z)$$

$$+ \mathbf{A}_R(z,\tau)|^2 + [\tilde{p}_z(t_0,\tau)^{1/2}/m_0^2 c^4]\}^{1/2}, \quad (59\text{a})$$

$$\tau(t_0,z) = t_0 + \int_0^z \frac{\gamma[z',\tau(t_0,z')]}{\tilde{p}_z[t_0,\tau(t_0,z')]}dz', \quad (59\text{b})$$

$$|\mathbf{A}_w(z) + \mathbf{A}_R(z,\tau)|^2$$

$$= A_w^2(z) + A_R^2(z)$$

$$+ 2A_w(z)A_R(z)\cos\{\theta_p[z,\tau(t_0,z)]\}. \quad (59\text{c})$$

The nonlinear formulation of the FEL is fully described by Eqs. (56)–(58). The ponderomotive potential plays a central role in axially bunching the electron. From Eq. (58) we see that this potential is given by

$$\Phi_{\text{pond}}(z,t) = (-|e|/\gamma m_0 c^2)A_w(z)A_R(z)$$

$$\times \cos\{\theta_p[z,\tau(t_0,z)]\}. \quad (60)$$

37

The amplitude and phase of the scattered fields as well as the axial beam momentum all vary with a characteristic axial length that is much longer than the wiggler wavelength λ_w. This fact allows for inexpensive numerical simulations to be performed in the laboratory frame with extremely high energy electron beams.

D. Coupled pendulum and wave equations

At this point our equations can be simplified and written in a more conventional form. To this end we define the electron's phase, ψ, with respect to the ponderomotive potential,

$$\psi(\psi_0,z) = \int_0^z \left(k(z') + k_w(z') - \frac{\omega}{\tilde{v}_z(\psi_0,z)} \right) dz' + \psi_0, \quad (61)$$

where $\psi_0 = -\omega t_0$ is the electron's phase upon entering the interaction region at $z = 0$ and ψ is also a function of the initial value $\partial\psi/\partial z|_{z=0}$. The second derivative of the electron's phase is

$$\frac{d^2\psi(\psi_0,z)}{dz^2} = \frac{d}{dz}(k_w + k) + \frac{\omega}{\tilde{v}_z^2(\psi_0,z)} \frac{d\tilde{v}_z(\psi_0,z)}{dz}. \quad (62)$$

Substituting (58) into (62) and assuming $\gamma \gg 1$, $|A_w| \gg |A_R|$, and $v_z \simeq \omega/(k + k_w) \simeq c$, we find the following pendulum equation:

$$\frac{d^2\psi}{dz^2} = \frac{d}{dz}(k_w + k) - \frac{|e|^2}{m_0^2 c^4} \frac{k_w}{\gamma_1^2} \frac{d}{dz} A_w^2$$

$$+ \frac{4|e|^2}{m_0^2 c^4} \frac{k_w^2}{\gamma_1^2} \left(A_w A_R \sin\psi - \frac{\gamma m_0 c^2}{|e|} \right.$$

$$\left. \times (\Phi_1 \sin\psi - \Phi_2 \cos\psi) \right), \quad (63)$$

38

where $\gamma_\perp = [1 + (|e|A_w/m_0c^2)^2]^{1/2}$ is the relativistic mass factor associated with the transverse wiggle motion. In the absence of space-charge effects, (63) reduces to the usual pendulum equation with a tapered wiggler[43] and without tapering.[31] Using the same assumptions as used to obtain the pendulum equation we find that

$$\left(\frac{\omega^2}{c^2} - k^2(z)\right)A_R(z) = \frac{\omega_b^2}{c^2}A_w(z)F\left\langle\frac{\cos\psi(\psi_0,z)}{\gamma(z,\psi_0)}\right\rangle, \quad (64a)$$

$$k^{1/2}(z)\frac{d}{dz}[A_R(z)k^{1/2}(z)]$$

$$= \frac{-\omega_b^2}{2x^2}A_w(z)F\left\langle\frac{\sin\psi(\psi_0,z)}{\gamma(z,\psi_0)}\right\rangle, \quad (64b)$$

$$\Phi_1(z) = (2\omega_b^2/\omega^2)(m_0c^2/\omega^2|e|)\langle\cos\psi(\psi_0,z)\rangle, \quad (64c)$$

$$\Phi_2(z) = (2\omega_b^2/\omega^2)(m_0c^2/|e|)\langle\sin\psi(\psi_0,z)\rangle, \quad (64d)$$

where $\langle\cdots\rangle = \int_0^{2\pi}(\cdots)d\psi_0/2\pi$ represents the ensemble average over the initial phases of the electrons. Equations (63) (64) represent the full set of nonlinear equations describing the one-dimensional FEL process with space-charge effects and tapered wiggler. In the limit when space-charge effects can be neglected, i.e., $\Phi_1 = \Phi_2 = 0$, Eqs. (63), (64a), and (64b) become equivalent to the KMR equations derived by Kroll et al.[43]

E. Numerical results in the Raman regime

In this section we present numerical results [39] for the coupled nonlinear FEL equations in (63) and (64). We assume that a monoenergetic electron beam enters the interaction region at $z = 0$ with a uniform density. The magnetic wiggler field given in (41) is assumed to be built up adiabatically from $z \leqslant 0$ to its initial value at $z = 0$. In all of our numerical simulations a small amplitude radiation field is introduced as a perturbation at $z = 0$ and allowed to grow spatially and self-consistently according to the FEL equations.

We first consider the case where the magnetic wiggler parameters are fixed, i.e., constant amplitude and period. Later we consider the case where the wiggler period is adiabatically decreased, resulting in substantially higher radiation efficiency.

In this example submillimeter radiation at $\lambda = 338\,\mu m$ using a 2.6 MeV electron beam. Table II lists the salient parameters for the wiggler field electron beam and output radiation. The magnetic wiggler amplitude, 2.5 kG, and the period is fixed at 2.0 cm. The 2.6 MeV ($\gamma_0 = 6$), 5 kA electron beam has a transverse equilibrium velocity of $v_w = 0.078c$.

Figure 5 shows the amplitude of the vector potential of the excited radiation, $A_R(z)$, and the spatial growth rate, $\Gamma = \partial[\ln A_R(z)]/\partial z$, function of z. These plots are for the frequency $\omega = 2\gamma_z^2 c k_w = 5 \times 10^{12}\,\text{sec}^{-1}$ ($\lambda = 338\,\mu m$). The region where the growth rate is constant is the linear or small-signal regime. Figure 6 shows the amplitude of the beam space-charge wave and the ponderomotive wave as a function of the interaction distance. Both wave amplitudes are of the same order of magnitude signifying that the process is for the most part in the Raman regime. Figure 7 shows the evolution of the wavenumber associated with the radiation field. Since the radiation wavenumber is greater than ω/c, the region is greater than unity. This implies that the radiation field will tend to focus inward toward the electron

Table II — Raman REL in the Submillimeter Regime
with Constant Magnetic Wiggler Parameters

Magnetic Wiggler Parameters		
Wiggler Wavelength	λ_w	2.0 cm
Wiggler Amplitude	B_w	2.5 kG
Electron Beam Parameters		
Beam Energy	E_b	2.6 MeV ($\gamma_0 = 6$)
Beam Current	I_b	5 kA
Axial Gamma	γ_{z0}	5.4
Beam Radius	r_b	0.3 cm
Wiggle Velocity	β_w	0.078
Self Potential Energy Spread	$\Delta E/E_0$	5.0%
Output Radiation Parameters		
Radiation Wavelength	λ	338 μm
Linear e-folding length*	$L_e = 1/\Gamma$	5.3 cm
Efficiency*	η	9.2%
Radiation Power*	P	1.2 GW

*At the maximum growth rate.

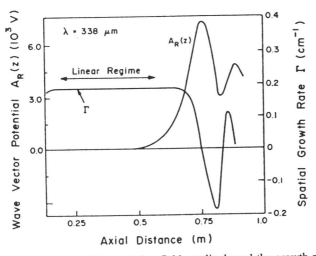

Fig. 5 — Evolution of the radiation field amplitude and the growth rate
as a function of the interaction distance

41

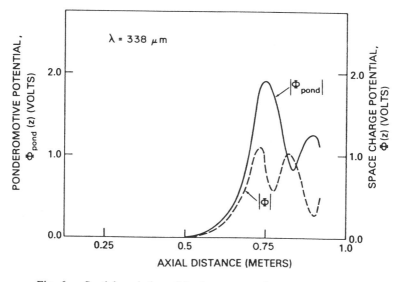

Fig. 6 — Spatial evolution of the beam space charge wave and ponder-omotive wave amplitude. This illustration is for the Raman regime.

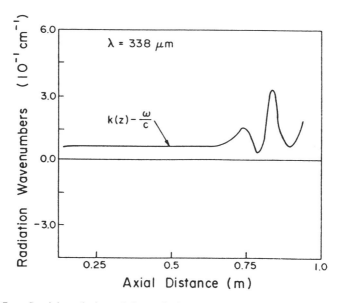

Fig. 7 — Spatial evolution of the radiation wave number; the range where k is constant is the linear regime. Since $k > \omega/c$ the radiation field will focus inward toward the electron beam.

42

beam. Figure 8 shows a comparison between the linear growth rate obtained from the dispersion relation in (24) (solid curve) with the growth rate obtained from the linear regime of the fully nonlinear simulations [crosses ($\times$)]. Also in this figure the theoretical efficiency based on Eq. (35) (dashed curve) is compared with the nonlinear results [circles (O)].

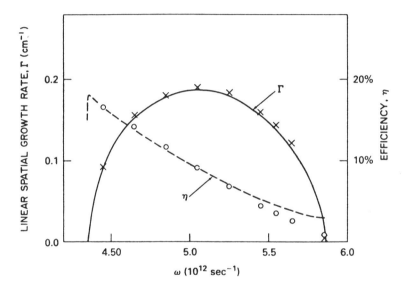

Fig. 8 — Comparison between the linear growth rate obtained from the dispersion relation (solid curve) and that obtained from the simulations in the linear regime (crosses (x)). Also shown is the theoretical efficiency based on Eq. (35) (dashed curve) compared with the nonlinear simulations (circles (O)).

F. Efficiency enhancement[39–43]

The phase velocity of the total longitudinal wave potential, i.e., ponderomotive plus space-charge is approximately

$v_{\mathrm{ph}} = \omega/(k + k_w)$. The longitudinal wave potential is responsible for axially bunching and eventually trapping the electrons. If the wiggler period is held fixed, the radiation field reaches its maximum value when the electrons are trapped in the longitudinal potential wells. Just prior to the saturation of the radiation field, the electrons are spatially bunched and trapped in the wave potential. The trapped electrons at this point can be considered, for our purpose, to form a macroparticle. By appropriately reducing the phase velocity as a function of axial distance down the interaction region, the kinetic energy of this macroparticle can be further reduced and converted into wave energy. The phase velocity must be reduced in such a way that the inertial potential of the trapped macroparticle is always less than the potential of the growing longitudinal wave. The phase velocity can be reduced by decreasing the period of the magnetic pump as a function of z. In order for the macroparticle to remain trapped, the spatial rate of change of the wiggler period must be sufficiently slow. In principle, virtually all the kinetic energy of the macroparticle can be extracted and converted to wave energy. However, not all the beam particles comprise the macroparticle; some may be untrapped. Converting particle kinetic energy into radiation by varying the wave velocity is somewhat analogous to the reverse process of particle acceleration in, say, a rf linac. Figure 9 illustrates the effect on the saturated radiation amplitude using a tapered wiggler field. In this figure the wiggler period is gradually decreased spatially at the point where the electrons are deeply trapped. Once the electrons are deeply trapped they are decelerated by decreasing the wiggler period. Figure 9 demonstrates that dramatic enhancements in the FEL efficiency can be achieved in this way.[39] (The parameters of Fig. 9 are different from Table II, and they are

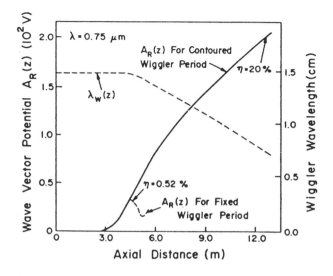

Fig. 9 — Efficiency enhancement by tapering the wiggler period

given in Ref. 39.) There are of course other schemes for enhancing efficiency in the FEL. These include, for example, spatially decreasing the wiggler amplitude[43] and/or applying an axial accelerating force such as a static electric field[48,54] to the trapped electrons.

These efficiency enhancement techniques are most effective when the injected electron beam is cold. The phase area displacement (PAD) method of FEL operation is a scheme for exploiting a variable parameter wiggler in conjunction with a circulating electron beam to enhance the gain achievable from a warm electron beam driver. This scheme has been proposed by Kroll *et al.*[43,118]

The PAD technique is illustrated schematically in Fig. 10, reproduced from Ref. 42. The shaded area of the diagram represents the (γ, ψ) phase space area occupied by electrons,

45

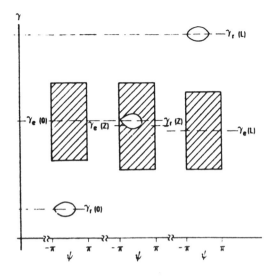

Fig. 10 — Motion of empty buckets through electron phase space in a phase area displacement FEL. (Reproduced from Ref. 42.)

while the oval buckets represent the separatrix boundaries of the ponderomotive potential that would enclose confined orbits for a "new" electron born within this region.

However, in the operational mode of phase area displacement, electrons are not actually trapped in the ponderomotive buckets. Instead, the ponderomotive wave is first established with resonant buckets located in the empty region of phase space below the region occupied by electrons. The wiggler parameters are then varied as one moves through the wiggler, such that the resonant energy γ_r of the empty bucket is accelerated upward through the phase area occupied by the beam. As this happens, the electron phase space trajectories carry the electrons around the bucket in a clockwise direction. The net result is that the entire phase

46

area occupied by the electrons is ultimately displaced downward in energy during each pass. At the same time, the final energy spread of the beam is nearly equal to the inital energy spread.

This mechanism of phase area displacement can cause all of the electrons to be decelerated, even when the initial energy spread is considerably larger than the bucket height. As long as the total change in γ_r is much larger than the sum of the bucket height and the energy spread in the beam, the average energy loss of the electrons will be independent of the initial energy spread in the beam. In order that the increase in the energy spread remains small, it is necessary that the phase area occupied by the buckets be kept constant during the acceleration.

In Fig. 11, also reproduced from Ref. 42, results are plotted of the average energy loss and the energy spread of the electrons as a function of the number of passes through the FEL. For this particular numerical study, the electron equations of motion are integrated as the same electron beam is passed through the FEL many times. Between passes, an equal amount of energy was added to all electrons to replace energy lost to the electromagnetic wave; in addition, the phase of each electron is randomized between passages. This simulates a cyclic system in which energy can be resupplied to the electrons between passes. It may be noted that the buildup rate for the energy spread is much slower than the rate of energy lost, whereas for the case of a constant parameter wiggler, these rates are comparable. It also appears that this phase area displacement mode of operation should not be afflicted with the problem of sideband instabilities, since the electrons are not trapped within the ponderomotive buckets.

47

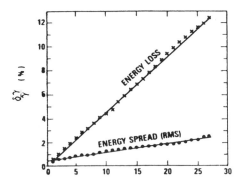

Fig. 11 — The average energy loss and the energy spread of the electrons as a function of the number of passes through an FEL. (Reproduced from Ref. 42.)

When the electron beam is warm, the growth rate is proportional to the slope of the distribution function, and the growth is due to those particles that are in resonance with the ponderomotive wave. The nonlinear saturation of the FEL by quasilinear processes has been considered by Dimos and Davidson.[115]

IV. THREE-DIMENSIONAL THEORY OF FREE-ELECTRON LASERS

Thus far our analysis of the FEL has been limited to one dimension, i.e., along the dominant direction of motion of the electrons. The one-dimensional model, however, has a limited usefulness. For example, an important multidimensional effect in FEL's is optical guiding of the generated radiation beam. Optical guiding plays a central role in the practical realization of high power, short wavelength FEL's. This phenomenon can allow the radiation beam to propagate over long distances without substantial transverse spreading.

The purpose of this section is to formulate a multidimensional theory of the FEL. This formulation includes the transverse dependence of both the radiation beam as well as the particle orbits. The analysis is supplemented by a numerical example illustrating the phenomenon of optical guiding.

A. Optical guiding

Diffraction is a fundamental phenomenon in wave optics and refers to the natural tendency of a radiation beam to spread laterally as it propagates. One of the successes of FEL theory was the prediction that the resonant interaction between the optical field and the electron beam can result in optical guiding. In certain regimes optical guiding may make it possible to maintain a significant overlap between the optical beam and the electron beam, leading to enhanced gain and extraction efficiency.

In a FEL, optical guiding may be considered to arise from two distinct characteristics of the medium. Refractive guiding, which is described by the reactive (real) part of the refractive index, is due to the phase shift of light, as is indicated by the fact that $v_{\text{phase}} < c$.[37,39,43,45] This type of guiding is similar to that occurring in optical fibers and was studied for the low-gain FEL by Sprangle and Tang.[54] This was the first analysis indicating the possibility of guiding when multidimensional effects are properly taken into account. The other type of guiding, gain focusing, is described by the imaginary part of the refractive index.

Gain focusing does not modify the radiation wave fronts and thus power diffracts away from the laser beam. However, if the gain of the FEL is sufficient to replenish the diffracted power, then the laser beam can propagate undistorted in form. On the other hand, refractive guiding causes the wave fronts to be distorted, tending to redirect the radiation power flow toward the electron beam and along the direction of propagation.

Gain focusing is especially important in the small-signal FEL regime. Moore was the first to show that in the high-gain, small-signal regime it is possible for the radiation to propagate without transverse spreading.[55] Specifically, for a sharp-edge electron beam and an azimuthally symmetric system, he obtained solutions of the wave equation that were self-similar (i.e., undistorted in form) but exponentially growing along the axial direction. Scharlemann et al.[56] exploited the analogy with an optical fiber using a complex refractive index to study the growth of optically guided modes. Numerical solutions of the two-dimensional FEL equations and more general analyses confirmed the constancy of the radiation profile.[56,57,119-121] When the radiation field amplitude is sufficiently large electrons become trapped in the ponderomotive well and the growth of the radiation amplitude ceases to be exponential. In this stage, referred to as the trapped-particle regime, the gain may be small and refractive guiding can dominate gain focusing.

In order to motivate the following analysis we shall briefly present a simple model of the optical guiding phenomenon. For this purpose let us consider a FEL operating in the small-signal, high-gain Compton regime, with the dispersion relation being given by Eq. (26). Noting that the maximum spatial growth rate is obtained when k_{em} is equal to $(\omega - k_w v_{z0})/v_{z0}$, the solution to the dispersion relation may be written as

$$n = 1 - \frac{\omega_b^2}{2\gamma_0\omega^2} + F^{1/3}\left(\frac{\omega_b^2\beta_w^2 ck_w}{2\gamma_0\omega^3}\right)^{1/3}\frac{1 - i\sqrt{3}}{2}, \quad (65)$$

where $n = ck/\omega$ is the (complex-valued) refractive index. The imaginary part of n represents the (exponential) growth of the radiation field amplitude. This is the basis for gain focusing of the optical field. The first three terms in the expression for the refractive index are real and thus represent the phase shift of the excited radiation field in the FEL. In a complete multidimensional analysis, taking into account the transverse dependence of electron beam density, the first term would represent vacuum diffraction of the optical field. The second term would lead to refraction of light away from the electron beam as one would expect in an unmagnetized plasma. The third term is due to the resonant FEL coupling and is responsible for optical guiding. The third term exceeds the second when

$$\beta_w > \frac{1}{\sqrt{2}}\frac{\gamma_z}{\gamma_0}\frac{\omega_b^2}{\omega^2}F^{-1/2}, \quad (66)$$

which is easily satisfied in the high-gain Compton regime [see (28)]. If (66) is satisfied the radiation will tend to focus in the vicinity of the electron beam. However, the heuristic nature of this argument must be emphasized since it is based on a one-dimensional model of the FEL interaction. The remainder of this section is therefore devoted to a self-consistent analysis of FEL's and optical guiding, taking into account the multidimensional nature of the problem.

In order to understand and analyze the phenomenon of optical guiding as it pertains to free-electron lasers, we first consider the vacuum diffraction of a plane wave with a Gaussian transverse profile. We then generalize our description to the case of an arbitrary beam propagating in vacuum, in the absence of a source (driving current). Next, we examine the case, such as a free-electron laser, where the source modifies the vacuum propagation characteristics of the Gaussian modes to such an extent that for an accurate description of the propagation of the beam a large number of eigenmodes are required. Finally we outline the method of source-dependent expansion of Sprangle et al.[57,119] This method self-consistently incorporates the source function into the propagation characteristics of the eigenmodes. This method of solving the wave equation affords a highly simplified, elegant, and numerically fast description of the evolution of the optical field.

B. Vacuum diffraction[122]

Let us begin by considering a plane, parallel radiation beam of infinite cross section incident on an opaque screen with a finite circular aperture of radius a. As is well known the optical field beyond the screen consists of an expanding set of curved wave fronts. The radiation is approximately confined to a cone of half-angle $\Theta_d = \pi^{-1}\lambda/a$, the diffraction angle.

It is easy to see why diffraction could provide a fundamental limit on the gain and extraction obtainable in a free-electron laser. For example, suppose that at $z = 0$ the radiation beam and the fixed radius electron beam both have a radius equal to $r_s(0)$. Then, beyond a distance on the order of

$$z \sim r_s(0)/\Theta_d = \pi r_s^2(0)/\lambda, \tag{67}$$

the diffraction of the optical beam leads to a substantial reduction in the overlap between the optical field and the electrons. In other words, the filling factor is significantly reduced.

The Gaussian form is fundamental in the description of propagation of light beams. In a vacuum the vector potential of the laser beam is expressible as

$$\mathbf{A}_R(r,z,t) = \tfrac{1}{2}A(r,z)\exp[i(\omega z/c - \omega t)]\tilde{e}_x + \text{c.c.,} \qquad (68a)$$

where

$$A(r,z) = |A(r,z)|\exp[i\phi(r,z)] \qquad (68b)$$

is the complex amplitude and $\omega = 2\pi c/\lambda$ is the frequency. Under certain generally valid approximations the form (68) is a solution of the wave equation in vacuum when the amplitude $|A|$ and phase ϕ are given by

$$|A| = A_0[r_{s0}/r_s(z)]\exp[-r^2/r_s^2(z)], \qquad (69a)$$

$$\phi(r,z) = \pi r^2/\lambda R(z) - \tan^{-1}(z/z_R) + \phi_0, \qquad (69b)$$

where A_0 and ϕ_0 are constants and $R(z)$ is the radius of curvature of the wave fronts. The quantity $r_s(z)$ is the width or the "spot size" of the beam at z. The spot size is related to the minimum spot size (waist) r_{s0} at $z = 0$, via

$$r_s(z) = r_{s0}[1 + (z/z_R)^2]^{1/2}. \qquad (70)$$

The Rayleigh range is defined by

$$z_R = \pi r_{s0}^2/\lambda, \qquad (71)$$

and is the scale length for the lateral spreading out of the optical beam. The Rayleigh range defined in (71) is seen to be identical to the diffraction scale length in (67) derived on purely heuristic grounds. In terms of z_R, the radius of curvature of the wave fronts evolves as

$$R = z[1 + (z_R/z)^2]. \qquad (72)$$

Thus the wave fronts are planar at $z = 0$ and spherical for $|z| \gg z_R$.

In conclusion it should be emphasized that, in vacuum, a radiation beam that initially has a Gaussian variation in the transverse direction maintains that same functional dependence. The propagation effects appear in the parameters such as the spot size $r_s(z)$ and the radius of curvature $R(z)$.

C. Analysis of radiation focusing and guiding

For propagation in a more general environment the distortion of the optical beam may be so severe that its representation in terms of the fundamental vacuum Gaussian modes (with spatially varying parameters) becomes inadequate. The conventional approach is to enlarge the set of functions by using higher-order vacuum Laguerre–Gaussian modes. In circumstances where the driving current greatly modifies the vacuum propagation characteristics of the system, a large number of vacuum Laguerre–Gaussian modes must be summed up to represent accurately the radiation field.

Considerable progress and simplification in the analysis of propagation of radiation was made by the development of the source-dependent expansion (SDE) technique.[57] The novel aspect of the SDE method is that the characteristics of the modes are governed by the driving current density as opposed to the heuristic, vacuum-mode expansion technique. Instead of using the usual modal expansion in terms of the vacuum Laguerre–Gaussian functions, the source function (driving current) is self-consistently incorporated into the evolution of the spot size, wave front curvature, and the amplitude of the radiation field. As a result the new fundamental mode remains dominant throughout the evolution of the optical field.

54

To proceed we generalize the wave equation (3) to

$$\left[\frac{1}{r}\frac{\partial}{\partial r}\left(r\frac{\partial}{\partial r}\right)+\frac{1}{r^2}\frac{\partial^2}{\partial\theta^2}+\frac{\partial^2}{\partial z^2}-\frac{1}{c^2}\frac{\partial^2}{\partial t^2}\right]\mathbf{A}_R=-\frac{4\pi}{c}\mathbf{J},$$
(73)

where $\mathbf{J}$ is the current density. As usual, we assume the vector potential of the optical beam is expressible as the product of a rapidly oscillating phase factor and a slowly varying complex envelope:

$$\mathbf{A}_R(r,\theta,z,t)=\tfrac{1}{2}A(r,\theta,z)\exp[i(\omega z/c-\omega t)]\hat{e}_x+\text{c.c.}$$
(74)

Substituting (74) into (73) leads to the following reduced wave equation:

$$\left[\frac{1}{r}\frac{\partial}{\partial r}\left(r\frac{\partial}{\partial r}\right)+\frac{1}{r^2}\frac{\partial}{\partial\theta^2}+2i\frac{\omega}{c}\frac{\partial}{\partial z}\right]a(r,\theta,z)=S(r,\theta,z),$$
(75)

where $a(r,\theta,z)=|e|A/m_0c^2=|a|\exp(i\phi)$ is the normalized complex radiation field amplitude, and the source function S has the general form

$$S(r,\theta,z)=(\omega^2/c^2)[1-n^2(r,\theta,z,a)]a(r,\theta,z), \qquad (76)$$

where $n(r,\theta,z,a)$ is the amplitude-dependent, complex refractive index.

Equation (75), which is referred to as the reduced or parabolic wave equation, is often used to describe wave propagation phenomena since, by virtue of the absence of the second derivative in z, it simplifies the solution of the wave equation. As such it also incorporates the basic assumption that the optical beam is comprised of waves propagating predominantly along the z axis.

55

Next we choose the following representation for $a(r,\theta,z)$ in terms of the associated Laguerre polynomials:

$$a(r,\theta,z) = \sum_{m,p} C_{m,p}(\theta,z) D_m^p(r), \qquad (77)$$

where $m,p = 0,1,2,...,$

$$C_{m,p}(\theta,z) = a_{m,p}(z)\cos(p\theta) + b_{m,p}(z)\sin(p\theta), \quad (78)$$

$$D_m^p(r) = \xi^{p/2} L_m^p(\xi)\exp\{-[1-i\alpha(z)]\xi/2\}, \quad (79)$$

where $\xi = 2r^2/r_s^2(z)$.

In Eqs. (77)–(79), $a_{m,p}(z)$ and $b_{m,p}(z)$ are complex, $r_s(z)$ is the spot size of the optical beam, $\alpha(z)$ is related to the curvature of the wave fronts, and $L_m^p(z)$ is the associated Laguerre polynomial. The crucial z dependence of the parameters is to be determined by solving Eq. (75) with a given source function S.

Substituting (77) into (75) and using the orthogonality properties of L_m^p, $\cos(p\theta)$, and $\sin(p\theta)$, we obtain

$$\left(\frac{\partial}{\partial z} + A_{m,p}(z)\right)\begin{bmatrix} a_{m,p} \\ b_{m,p} \end{bmatrix} - imB(z)\begin{bmatrix} a_{m-1,p}(z) \\ b_{m-1,p}(z) \end{bmatrix}$$

$$- i(m+p+1)B^*(z)\begin{bmatrix} a_{m+1,p}(z) \\ b_{m+1,p}(z) \end{bmatrix}$$

$$= -i\begin{bmatrix} F_{m,p}(z) \\ G_{m,p}(z) \end{bmatrix}, \qquad (80)$$

where

$$A_{m,p}(z) = \frac{r_s'}{r_s} + i(2m+p+1)\left(\frac{(1+\alpha^2)c}{\omega r_s^2} - \frac{\alpha r_s'}{r_s} + \frac{\alpha'}{2}\right), \qquad (81a)$$

$$B(z) = -\left(\frac{\alpha r_s'}{r_s} + \frac{(1-\alpha^2)c}{\omega r_s^2} - \frac{\alpha'}{2}\right) - i\left(\frac{r_s'}{r_s} - \frac{2\alpha c}{\omega r_s^2}\right),$$

(81b)

where the prime denotes $\partial/\partial z$, and

$$\begin{bmatrix} F_{m,p}(z) \\ G_{m,p}(z) \end{bmatrix} = \frac{c}{2\pi\omega} \frac{m!}{(m+p)!} \int_0^{2\pi} d\theta \int_0^{\infty} d\xi \, S(\xi,\theta,z)$$

$$\times [D_m^p(\xi)]^* \begin{bmatrix} (1+\delta_{p,0})^{-1}\cos(p\theta) \\ \sin(p\theta) \end{bmatrix}.$$

(81c)

The equation for $a_{m,p}$ and $b_{m,p}$ in (80) is undetermined since the function $B(z)$ is arbitrary. If we choose $B=0$, we would in effect be expanding the radiation field in the conventional vacuum Laguerre–Gaussian modes. A more appropriate choice for $B(z)$ will depend on the particular problem under consideration. Let us consider one of the most common situations where the radiation beam at $z=0$ is known and has a Gaussian radial profile symmetric about the z axis. In this case the complex radiation amplitude at $z=0$ is given by

$$a(r,\theta,0) = a_{0,0} \exp\{-[1-i\alpha(0)]r^2/r_s^2(0)\}, \quad (82)$$

and is independent of θ. Let us further assume that for $z>0$ the radiation beam profile remains approximately Gaussian with a nearly circular cross section. That is, the dominant part of the source $S(r,\theta,z)$ has an r and z dependence and the θ-dependent part is weak. In this case we expect the magnitude of the coefficients, $a_{m,p}(z)$ and $b_{m,p}(z)$, to become progressively smaller as m and p take on larger values, i.e., $|a_{m,p}| \gg |a_{m+1,p}|, |a_{m,p+1}|$ and $|b_{m,p}| \gg |b_{m+1,p}|, |b_{m,p+1}|$. The lowest-order approximation to the radiation beam is given by the $a_{0,0}(z)$ mode. Hence if the $a_{0,0}$ mode gives a good approximation to the radiation field we may solve for $a_{0,0}(z)$, $r_s(z)$, and $\alpha(z)$ using (80). From (80) we find that only the $m = 0,1$ and $p = 0$ equations are relevant and yield

$$\left(\frac{\partial}{\partial z} + A_{0,0}\right)a_{0,0} = -iF_{0,0}, \tag{83a}$$

$$Ba_{0,0} = F_{1,0}. \tag{83b}$$

We now have a specific expression for $B(z)$, from (83b), in terms of one of the moments, $F_{1,0}$, of the source term. Substituting (81b) into $B(z) = F_{1,0}(z)/a_{0,0}(z)$ yields the following first-order coupled differential equations for r_s and α:

$$r_s' - 2c\alpha/\omega r_s = -r_s(F_{1,0}/a_{0,0})_I, \tag{84a}$$

$$\alpha' - \frac{2(1+\alpha^2)c}{\omega r_s^2} = 2\left[\left(\frac{F_{1,0}}{a_{0,0}}\right)_R - \alpha\left(\frac{F_{1,0}}{a_{0,0}}\right)_I\right], \tag{84b}$$

where $(\ )_{R,I}$ denotes the real and imaginary part of the enclosed function. Since $r_s(z)$ and $\alpha(z)$ are now known from (84a) and (84b), we may solve for $A_{m,p}(z)$ using (81a),

$$A_{m,p}(z) = 2c\alpha/\omega r_s^2 - (F_{1,0}/a_{0,0})_I$$
$$+ i(2m + p + 1)[2c/\omega r_s^2 + (F_{1,0}/a_{0,0})_R]. \tag{85}$$

Using $B(z) = F_{1,0}(z)/a_{0,0}(z)$ and the resulting equations for r_s and α in (84a) allows us to solve for $a_{m,p}$ and $b_{m,p}$ in (80).

It is useful at this point to consider the simple case of propagation of a radiation beam in vacuum (no source term). To illustrate this well-known limit we evaluate $a_{m,p}$, $b_{m,p}$, r_s, and α in the source-free case, $F_{m,p} = G_{m,p} = B = 0$.

Equations (84a) and (84b) become $r_s'' = (2c/\omega)^2 r_s^3$ and $\alpha = (\omega/2c) r_s r_s'$ and have the solutions

$$r_s(z) = r_s(0)(1 + z^2/z_R^2)^{1/2}, \tag{86a}$$

$$\alpha(z) = z/z_R, \tag{86b}$$

where $r_s(0)$ is the minimum radiation spot size at $z = 0$, $z_R = (\omega/2c) r_s^2(0) = \pi r_s^2(0)/\lambda$ is the Rayleigh length, and $\lambda = 2\pi c/\omega$ is the wavelength. From (85) we find that $A_{m,p}(z) = 2[\alpha(z) + i(2m + p + 1)] c\omega r_s^2(z)$, which allows us to solve for $a_{m,p}$ and $b_{m,p}$ using (80),

$$\begin{pmatrix} a_{m,p}(z) \\ b_{m,p}(z) \end{pmatrix} = \begin{pmatrix} a_{m,p}(0) \\ b_{m,p}(0) \end{pmatrix} \begin{pmatrix} r_s(0) \\ r_s(z) \end{pmatrix}$$

$$\times \exp\left[-i(2m + p + 1)\tan^{-1}\left(\frac{z}{z_R}\right)\right]. \tag{87}$$

Equations (86a), (86b), and (87), together with the representations in (77)–(79), are in agreement with the conventional vacuum Gaussian–Laguerre form in (69) and (70).

D. Radiation-beam envelope equation

To illustrate some of the interesting properties of the optical field in a free-electron laser we now consider the example of an axially symmetric electron beam propagating through a planar wiggler. Assuming a Gaussian density profile for the electron beam, the appropriate refractive index can be shown[45,54,56] to be given by

$$n(r,z,a) = 1 + \frac{1}{2} \frac{\omega_b^2(r,z)}{\omega^2} \left\langle \frac{e^{-i\psi}}{\gamma} \right\rangle \frac{a_w}{|a(r,z)|}, \tag{88}$$

where

$$\omega_b^2(r,z) = \omega_{b0}^2 [r_{b0}/r_b(z)]^2 \exp[-r^2/r_b^2(z)],$$

$r_b(z)$ is the electron beam radius, $r_{b0} = r_b(0)$, $\omega_{b0} = (4\pi|e|^2 n_{b0}/m_0)^{1/2}$ is the initial beam–plasma frequency on axis, n_{b0} is the initial beam density on axis, $a_w = |e|B_w/k_w m_0 c^2$ is the normalized wiggler amplitude, B_w is the wiggler magnetic field strength, k_w is the wiggler wavenumber, ψ is the electron's phase in the ponderomotive wave potential, and $\langle \ \rangle$ denotes the ensemble average over all electrons. Substituting (88) into (76) and noting that $|1 - n| \ll 1$ gives the FEL source function

$$S(r,z) = \frac{-\omega_b^2}{c^2} a_w \left\langle \frac{e^{-i\psi}}{\gamma} \right\rangle \frac{a(r,z)}{|a(r,z)|}. \tag{89}$$

Since the electron beam radius r_b may not be matched with respect to the focusing fields (wiggler gradients) and defocusing effects (beam emittance), we allow r_b to be a function of z. To proceed with the analysis we assume that in the source function the complex radiation field amplitude in (77) can be approximated by the lowest-order mode, $a_{0,0}(z) \exp[-(1 - i\alpha)r^2/r_s^2]$. With this assumption the source function can be written as

$$S(\xi,z) = -4\nu(a_w/r_b^2)$$

$$\times (a_{0,0}/|a_{0,0}|)\langle e^{-i\psi}/\gamma \rangle e^{-(r_s^2/r_b^2 - i\alpha)\xi/2}, \tag{90}$$

where $\nu = (\omega_{b0} r_{b0}/2c)^2 = I_b/17\beta_0$ is Budker's constant and I_b is the electron-beam current in kiloamperes. The moments of the source function, $F_{m,p}(z)$, are given by

$$F_{m,0} = -4 \frac{c}{\omega} \nu \left(\frac{a_w}{r_b^2}\right) \frac{a_{0,0}}{|a_{0,0}|} \left\langle \frac{e^{-i\psi}}{\gamma} \right\rangle \frac{(r_s^2/r_b^2 - 1)^m}{(r_s^2/r_b^2 + 1)^{m+1}}, \tag{91}$$

where we have assumed ψ to be constant across the electron beam. Since we are considering an axially symmetric electron beam and radiation field we note that $a_{m,p} = F_{m,p} = G_{m,p} = 0$ for $p > 0$. Substituting (91) into (84a), (84b), and (85) yields

$$r_s r_s' - 2c\alpha/\omega = -2(c/\omega)C(z)\langle \sin \psi \rangle, \tag{92a}$$

$$r_s^2 \alpha' - 2(1 + \alpha^2)c/\omega = -4(c/\omega)C(z)(\langle \cos \psi \rangle$$
$$+ \alpha \langle \sin \psi \rangle), \tag{92b}$$

$$A_{m,0}(z) = (2c/r_s^2\omega)\{\alpha + i(2m + 1)$$
$$- C(z)[\langle \sin \psi \rangle + i(2m + 1)\langle \cos \psi \rangle]\}, \tag{92c}$$

where $C(z) = (2v/\gamma)H(z)a_w/|a_{0,0}(z)|$, $H(z) = (1 - F)/(1 + F)^2$, and $F(z) = r_b^2/r_s^2$ is the filling factor. The function $C(z)$ measures the coupling between the radiation and electron beam and decreases as the radiation grows.

Equations (92a) and (92b) can be combined to give the following envelope equation for the radiation beam:

$$r_s'' + K^2(z,r_b,r_s,a_{0,0})r_s = 0, \tag{93a}$$

where the initial condition on r_s' is found from (92a) and

$$K^2 = (2c/\omega)^2(-1 + C^2\langle \sin \psi \rangle^2 + 2C \langle \cos \psi \rangle$$
$$+ (\omega/2c)r_s^2 C'\langle \sin \psi \rangle)r_s^{-4}. \tag{93b}$$

The first term on the right-hand side of (93b) is defocusing and corresponds to the usual diffraction expansion, the second and third terms are always focusing while the last term is usually a defocusing contribution.

Focusing occurs when $K^2 \geqslant 0$. In the high-gain trapped-particle regime, the condition for a perfectly guided beam ($K = 0$) cannot be maintained since K^2 decreases as the radiation grows. In the small-signal, exponential-gain regime the quantities $\langle \sin \psi \rangle$ and $\langle \cos \psi \rangle$ may be calculated from the linearized orbit equations. The envelope equation may then be solved to determine r_s as a function of distance along the wiggler.[119]

As a specific example, we present the results for the parameters given in Table III that are similar to those used in Ref. 123 in connection with experimental design parameters at LLNL. Figure 12 illustrates the phenomenon of optical guiding for an FEL operating in the small-signal, exponential-gain regime. It is found that, irrespective of the initial beam radius, the optical field asymptotes to a perfectly guided profile with a unique value of the spot size. The magnitude of the matched spot size can be shown to be given by a simple algebraic equation.[119]

E. Particle equations

In the previous subsection we considered a particular case in which the transverse electron beam profile was taken to be constant and Gaussian in form. Further approximations were made in evaluating the ensemble average $\langle e^{-i\psi} / \gamma \rangle$ so as to proceed with the analysis. A more sophisticated treatment of the FEL should include transverse particle dynamics. When this is coupled to the SDE equations for the optical field one is able to perform a thorough analysis of the FEL interaction.

Table III — Numerical Illustration of Optical Guiding,
Parameters Taken from Ref. 123

Electron beam	
Current	$I_b = 2$ kA ($\nu = 0.118$)
Energy	$E_b = 50$ MeV ($\gamma = 100$)
Radius	$r_{b0} = 0.3$ cm
Radiation	
Wavelength	$\gamma = 10.6$ μm
Initial spot size	$r_{s0} = 0.35, 0.24, 0.15$
Wiggler field	
Wavelength	$\lambda_w = 8$ cm
Wiggler strength	$B_w = 2.3$ kG ($a_w = 1.716$)

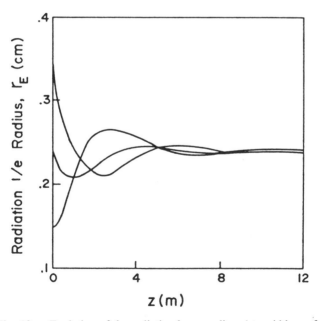

Fig. 12 — Evolution of the radiation beam radius, $1/e$ width r_E, for
various initial spot sizes (a) 0.35 cm, (b) 0.24 cm, and (c) 0.15 cm

For simplicity we shall assume that the optical field is azimuthally symmetric and the wiggler field is plane polarized,

$$A_w(y,z) = A_w \cosh(k_w y)\sin(k_w z)\hat{e}_x,$$

where A_w is the amplitude of the vector potential. After some simple algebra one finds that the equations of motion of the ith electron, of energy $\gamma_i mc^2$, are given by [68]

$$\frac{d\gamma_i}{dt} = \frac{i\omega a_w f_B}{4\gamma_i} \sum_n a_n L_n \left(\frac{2r_i^2}{r_s^2}\right)$$

$$\times \exp\left(i\psi_i - (1 - i\alpha)\frac{r_i^2}{r_s^2}\right) + \text{c.c.}, \qquad (94a)$$

$$\frac{d\psi_i}{dt} = ck_w - \frac{\omega}{2\gamma_i^2}\left(1 + \tfrac{1}{2}a_w^2 \cosh^2(k_w y_i) + \frac{\gamma_i^2(dy_i/dt)^2}{c^2}\right), \qquad (94b)$$

$$\frac{d^2 y_i}{dt^2} = -c^2 k_{\beta i}^2 y_i, \qquad (94c)$$

where r_i is the radial distance of the ith electron, $\psi_i = (\omega/c + k_w)z_i - \omega t$ is the relative phase, with z_i the axial location of the ith electron. The function $f_B \equiv J_0(\zeta) - J_1(\zeta)$, where $\zeta = (a_w/2)^2(1 + a_w^2/2)$, is a numerical factor that is less than unity and reduces the coupling strength in a planar wiggler. This reduction is due to the oscillatory component of the axial velocity of the particles at twice the wiggler wavenumber.[32,58] In Eq. (94c), which describes the betatron motion, y_i is the y coordinate and $k_{\beta i} = a_w k_w/\sqrt{2}\gamma_i$ is the betatron wavenumber of the ith electron.[123]

In conclusion, the full set of FEL equations consists of Eqs. (80), (81), and (84) for the optical field along with an appropriate summation over the particles, described by the equations of motion in Eq. (94). These equations constitute a multidimensional generalization of the KMR equations derived by Kroll et al.[43]

V. FREE-ELECTRON LASER THEORY IN THE PRESENCE OF AN AXIAL MAGNETIC FIELD

An axial solenoidal magnetic field is often used in FEL's driven by high current electron beams in order to assist in the confinement of the beam against the effects of self-fields. However, it has been shown, both in theory and experiments, that the axial field can have several beneficial effects upon the FEL interaction. In the first place, field immersed diodes have a clear advantage in the production of high quality electron beams,[85] which is a fundamental requirement for high efficiency FEL's. In the second place, the axial field can fundamentally alter the FEL interaction and provide for a resonant enhancement in both the gain and interaction efficiencies.

The introduction of an axial magnetic field in the FEL configuration was first proposed and analyzed by Sprangle et al.[30] One effect of the axial magnetic field is to enhance the transverse wiggle velocity.[30,82,83,114] The steady-state orbits in a helical wiggler field are modified by the presence of the axial field and can be driven unstable. In addition, the coupling is altered because of modifications to the dispersion of the interacting modes, and both the growth rate and saturation efficiency are affected. In fact, the combined effects of a helical wiggler and axial guide field can drive the beam space-charge mode linearly unstable.[124]

65

A. Steady-state orbits

The electron orbits in combined helical wiggler and axial guide fields have been extensively treated both in one-dimensional[83] and three-dimensional analyses.[114,124] The one-dimensional limit is valid when the displacement of the electron orbit from the axis of symmetry is much less than the wiggler period, which holds when the coupling coefficient (v_w/v_{z0}) is small. In this limit, the single-particle orbit equations take the form

$$\frac{dv_1}{dt} = -(\Omega_0 - k_w v_3)v_2, \tag{95a}$$

$$\frac{dv_2}{dt} = (\Omega_0 - k_w v_3)v_1 - \Omega_w v_3, \tag{95b}$$

$$\frac{dv_3}{dt} = \Omega_w v_2, \tag{95c}$$

where (v_1, v_2, v_3) are the components of the velocity in the wiggler frame defined by the basis,

$$\hat{e}_1 = \hat{e}_x \cos(k_w z) + \hat{e}_y \sin(k_w z),$$
$$\hat{e}_2 = -\hat{e}_x \sin(k_w z) + \hat{e}_y \cos(k_w z),$$

$\hat{e}_3 = \hat{e}_z$, and $\Omega_{0,w} = |eB_{0,w}/\gamma_0 m_0 c|$ are the electron cyclotron frequencies due to the axial guide and wiggler fields, respectively. Steady-state solutions are obtained by requiring that the temporal derivatives vanish. In this manner, steady-state solutions of the form $v_1 = v_w$, $v_2 = 0$, and $v_3 = v_{z0}$ are found, where

$$v_w = \Omega_w v_{z0}/(\Omega_0 - k_w v_{z0}). \tag{96}$$

In addition, conservation of energy implies that v_w and v_{z0} are related by

$$v_w^2 + v_{z0}^2 = (1 - \gamma_0^{-2})c^2. \tag{97}$$

Equations (96) and (97) can be solved for v_{z0} as a function of the wiggler and guide field parameters and the beam energy. A representative solution is shown in Fig. 13 in which we plot the axial velocity versus the guide magnetic field. Two distinct classes of trajectory are found, which we term Group I or Group II, depending on whether Ω_0 is less than or greater than $k_w v_{z0}$, respectively.

B. Orbit stability

The stability of these trajectories is determined by introducing a perturbation on the steady-state trajectories. Letting $v_1 = v_w + \delta v_1$, $v_2 = \delta v_2$, and $v_3 = v_{z0} + \delta v_z$, we obtain

$$\frac{d\delta v_1}{dt} = -(\Omega_0 - k_w v_{z0})\delta v_2, \tag{98a}$$

$$\frac{d\delta v_2}{dt} = (\Omega_0 - k_w v_{z0})\delta v_1 - \tilde{\beta}_w \Omega_0 \delta v_3, \tag{98b}$$

$$\frac{d\delta v_3}{dt} = \Omega_w \delta v_2, \tag{98c}$$

where $\tilde{\beta}_w = v_w/v_{z0}$. It follows from these equations that δv_2 satisfies

$$\left(\frac{d^2}{dt^2} + \overline{\Omega}^2\right)\delta v_2 = 0, \tag{99}$$

where

$$\overline{\Omega}^2 \equiv (\Omega_0 - k_w v_{z0})[(1 + \tilde{\beta}_w^2)\Omega_0 - k_w v_{z0}]. \tag{100}$$

Instability results whenever $\overline{\Omega}^2 < 0$. In the regime in which $\Omega_0 < k_w\, v_{z0}$ (Group I orbits), therefore, the instability criterion is

$$k_w v_{z0}/(1 + \tilde{\beta}_w^2) < \Omega_0 < k_w v_{z0}.$$

It is straightforward to show that in the opposite regime in which $\Omega_0 > k_w v_{z0}$ (Group II orbits) all trajectories are stable in the one-dimensional limit. The unstable regimes are indicated by the dashed lines in Fig. 13.

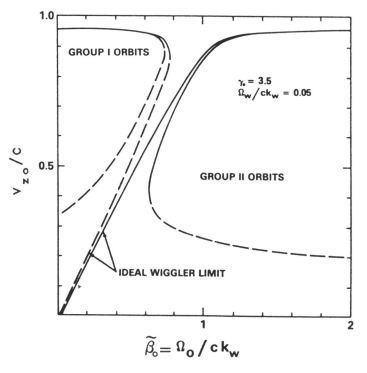

Fig. 13 — Axial velocity as a function of axial magnetic field. The one-dimensional case is labeled "ideal wiggler limit" and the three-dimensional case is shown for comparison

C. FEL dispersion relation in an axial magnetic field

Based upon the stable steady-state trajectories, a dispersion equation can be obtained in the one-dimensional limit.[84,125-128] We adopt the notation of Freund et al.[84] and write the linear dispersion equation in the form

$$[\omega^2 - k^2 c^2 - \omega_b^2 (\omega - k v_{z0})/\gamma_0 (\omega - \Omega_0 - k v_{z0})]$$
$$\times \{[\omega - (k + k_w) v_{z0}]^2 - \Phi_0 \omega_b^2/(\gamma_z^2 \gamma_0)\}$$
$$\simeq \Phi_0 \tilde{\beta}_w^2 (\omega_b^2/\gamma_0) c^2 k k_w, \qquad (101)$$

where

$$\Phi_0 \equiv 1 - \tilde{\beta}_w^2 \gamma_z^2 \Omega_0 / [(1 + \tilde{\beta}_w^2) \Omega_0 - k_w v_{z0}]. \qquad (102)$$

Note that the function Φ_0 goes to unity when either the axial magnetic field B_0 or the wiggler field B_w vanishes. In the limit of zero axial magnetic field, Eq. (101) reduces to the dispersion relation derived in the previous section, see Eq. (21).

The function Φ_0 can be seen to determine both the coupling constant and the effective plasma frequency of the beam space-charge wave. As shown in Fig. 14, $\Phi_0 \geqslant 1$ for stable Group I orbits. It is evident from the figure that Φ_0 increases monotonically with the axial field for Group I orbits and exhibits a singularity at the transition to orbital instability. Thus while the linear dispersion relation in (101) breaks down in the vicinity of the singularity, it is clear that the growth rate also increases with the axial field in this regime. However, for Group II orbits, Φ_0 is negative when

$$k_w v_{z0} < \Omega_0 < (\gamma_0/\gamma_2)^2 k_w v_{z0}. \qquad (103)$$

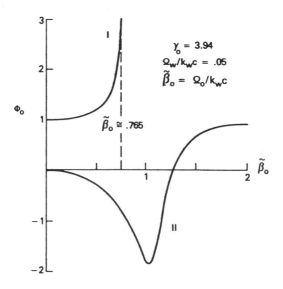

Fig. 14 — The magnetic coupling parameter Φ_0 vs axial magnetic field for both Group I and Group II orbits

The effect of Φ_0 negative on the interaction is significant and fundamentally alters the character of the FEL instability. Consideration of the uncoupled dispersion relation of the space-charge wave,

$$[\omega - (k + k_w)v_{z0}]^2 - \Phi_0\omega_b^2/(\gamma_z^2\gamma_0) = 0, \qquad (104)$$

shows that this mode is unstable[124] when $\Phi_0 < 0$. In order to explain this we consider the characteristics of the steady-state trajectories. In particular, it follows from (96) and (97) that

$$\frac{\partial v_{z0}}{\partial \gamma_0} = \frac{c^2}{\gamma_0\gamma_z^2v_{z0}}\Phi_0, \qquad (105)$$

which implies that the axial velocity tends to increase with decreases in the electron energy when $\Phi_0 < 0$. The increase in axial velocity is compensated for by a corresponding decrease in the transverse velocity. The result of this process is to provide a negative mass type of axial bunching mechanism that is the source of the space-charge instability. When $\Phi_0 > 0$ (which includes the limit in which there is no axial guide field) the FEL instability arises from the coupling of a negative energy space-charge wave and a positive energy electromagnetic wave. When $\Phi_0 < 0$, however, the coupling is between an unstable space-charge wave and an electromagnetic wave, and results in higher interaction efficiencies.

D. FEL growth rate in an axial magnetic field

For $\Phi_0 > 0$ the Raman or collective regime is obtained in the limit in which $\Gamma < \omega_b \Phi_0^{1/2} / \gamma_0^{1/2} \gamma_z v_{z0}$, where the peak growth rate is given by

$$\Gamma \simeq \tilde{\beta}_w \left[(\omega_b \gamma_z k_w / 4\gamma_0^{1/2} c) \Phi_0^{1/2} \right]^{1/2}. \tag{106}$$

The high-gain Compton regime is obtained when $\Gamma > \omega_b \Phi_0^{1/2} / \gamma_0^{1/2} \gamma_z v_{z0}$; in this regime the peak growth rate is given by

$$\Gamma \simeq \frac{\sqrt{3}}{2} \left(\frac{\tilde{\beta}_w^2}{2} \frac{\omega_b^2 k_w}{\gamma_0 c^2 \beta_{z0}} \Phi_0 \right)^{1/3} \tag{107}$$

In each case, growth occurs in a relatively narrow band about the resonant frequency $\omega \simeq 2\gamma_z^2 k_w v_{z0}$. The maximum growth rate for the Group I and Group II orbits is a function of the magnetic field. There can be a substantial enhancement in the linear growth rate for the Group I orbits. The source of the enhancement in the growth rate is twofold.

71

First, as the axial guide approaches a resonance with the wiggler field, i.e., as $\Omega_0 \sim k_w v_{z0}$, the transverse velocity becomes large. Second, as the transition to orbital instability at $\overline{\Omega}^2 = 0$ is approached $(1 + \tilde{\beta}_w^2)\Omega_0$ approaches $k_w v_{z0}$, at which point Φ_0 becomes singular. While the linear stability theory breaks down in the neighborhood of the singularity, it is evident that the coupling coefficient and hence, the growth rate increase as the transition to orbital instability is approached. The physical explanation for this derives from the fact that the electrons display a harmonic response at $\overline{\Omega}$, see Eq. (100), to the perturbation imposed by the ponderomotive potential. The ponderomotive potential acts as a slowly varying force at a frequency $\Delta\omega = \omega - 2\gamma_z^2 k_w v_{z0}$. Thus, in the vicinity of the orbital instability where $\overline{\Omega}$ is comparable to $|\Delta\omega|$, the ponderomotive force acts to drive the system near its natural response frequency, and large growth rates are obtained. In contrast, the Group II orbits with $\Phi_0 > 0$ exhibit no such enhancement in the growth rate. However, when $\Phi_0 < 0$ for the Group II orbits, a substantial enhancement in the growth rate is obtained.[84] This enhancement is due to a negative mass type of axial bunching mechanism that is the source of the space-charge instability.

The low-gain expression for the Compton regime can also be obtained in the presence of an axial guide field.[84,128] In this regime the gain is

$$G(z) = \frac{-\tilde{\beta}_w^2}{8} \frac{\omega_b^2 \Phi_0}{\gamma_0 c^2} k_w z^3 \frac{\partial}{\partial\theta}\left(\frac{\sin\theta}{\theta}\right)^2. \qquad (108)$$

The gain expression in Eq. (108) reduces to our previously derived result given by Eq. (32) in the limit of vanishing guide field and space-charge field. Since Φ_0 can be either positive or negative in the presence of an axial guide field, there are two distinct operating regimes. When $\Phi_0 > 0$ the qualitative character of the interaction is identical to that found in the absence of a guide field. However, when $\Phi_0 < 0$, gain is found for $\theta > 0$. In contrast to the positive Φ_0 regime, this implies that the phase velocity of the ponderomotive wave is greater than the axial velocity of the beam and is an expression of the negative mass effect described earlier. In addition, peak gain occurs when $\theta \simeq 1.3$, which also describes a frequency shift relative to the positive Φ_0 interaction. Additional analysis of the idealized one-dimensional model including a kinetic description of thermal effects is given in Ref. 129.

A fully three-dimensional analysis of the steady-state orbits in a combined helical wiggler and axial guide magnetic field has been given by Diament and Fajans et al.[114] Using these orbits, Freund and Ganguly[130] analyzed the linear stability of the TE and TM modes of a cylindrical waveguide. A three-dimensional nonlinear analysis and simulation have also been extensively analyzed including both thermal effects and efficiency enhancement by means of a tapered wiggler or guide magnetic field.[131,132]

VI. ELECTRON BEAM QUALITY

The electron beam voltage requirements for FEL's are modest in terms of the state of the art in accelerator technology. However, the beam current and beam quality at these required voltages present new challenges for accelerator scientists. The common parameters that characterize an electron beam are the voltage, current, and pulse length, from which the beam power and total energy can be obtained. More detailed knowledge about the beam dynamics requires additional information as to how the behavior differs from that of an ideal beam where all particles have identical motion (i.e., a cold monoenergetic beam). The departure from an ideal beam is often a result of nonlinearities, self-fields, and temperature effects.

The two most critical parameters that determine the quality of an electron beam in a FEL are the current and the effective energy spread. In general, the FEL gain and efficiency are increasing functions of beam current and decreasing functions of energy spread. Although the current and the effective energy spread are independent parameters in FEL theory, they are, in fact, related through the electron beam source. In any particular accelerator it is generally found that an increase in current results in an increase in effective energy spread. Hence the constraint on FEL scaling comes primarily from the accelerator. The manner in which beam quality affects the FEL interaction is determined by the particular operating regime. In general, the shorter the wavelength of the radiation the more demanding the requirements on the beam quality.

A. Beam emittance and radiation wavelength

Although the radiation and electron beam in the FEL are not constrained in the transverse direction by a slow wave structure or a waveguide, the beam profiles must be closely matched to ensure an efficient interaction. In this section we will compare the electron beam envelope with that of the radiation beam to obtain a simple heuristic relation between the radiation wavelength and beam emittance.

In the presence of an axial magnetic guide field the radial profile of an electron beam of current I_b can be obtained from the envelope equation[133,134]

$$\frac{\partial^2 r_b}{\partial z^2} + \frac{\Omega_0^2}{4\beta_0^2 c^2 \gamma_0^2} r_b - \frac{2\nu}{\beta_0^2 \gamma_0^3 r_b} - \frac{\epsilon_n^2 + (P_\theta/m_0 c)^2}{\beta_0^2 \gamma_0^2 r_b^3} = 0,$$

(109)

where Ω_0 is the nonrelativistic cyclotron frequency, $P_\theta = q\Psi_0/2\pi$, Ψ_0 is the magnetic flux linking the cathode, $\nu = (\omega_b r_b/2c)^2 = I_b[kA]/17\beta_0$ is Budker's parameter,

$$\epsilon_n = \beta_0 \gamma_0 \epsilon \simeq \beta_0 \gamma_0 r_b \langle \theta \rangle$$

(110)

is the normalized emittance, β_0 is the ratio of the beam velocity to the velocity of light, $\gamma_0 = (1 - \beta_0^2)^{-1/2}$ is the relativistic factor, r_b is the beam radius, and θ is the ratio of the perpendicular particle beam velocity to the parallel velocity. The second term on the left-hand side of Eq. (109) represents the inward magnetic pressure, the third term represents the outward self-field pressure, and the fourth term denotes the outward transverse effective thermal pressure. The brackets $\langle \; \rangle$ indicate that the root mean square is to be taken. Emittance is a measure of the product of the beam radius and the spread in the transverse velocity, i.e., emittance is proportional to the transverse phase space area.[133,134] In writing (109) and (110) we have assumed that the beam is symmetric and $\epsilon = \epsilon_x = \epsilon_y$, where the emittance is defined as

$$\epsilon_x = 4[\langle x^2 \rangle \langle (p_x/m_0 c)^2 \rangle - \langle xp_x/m_0 c \rangle^2]^{1/2},$$

x is the coordinate of a particle in the beam, and p_x is the momentum component in the x direction. This is the envelope, or edge emittance, of the beam and is a factor of 4 larger than the rms emittance.

The electron beam is said to be matched when the radius r_b is constant along z; i.e., when $\partial r_b/\partial z = 0$. For a matched beam the equilibrium radius is given by

$$r_b = \left(\frac{\nu}{\gamma_0}\left(\frac{2c}{\Omega_0}\right)^2 + \left\{\left(\frac{\nu}{\gamma_0}\right)^2\left(\frac{2c}{\Omega_0}\right)^4 \right.\right.$$
$$\left.\left. + \left(\frac{2c}{\Omega_0}\right)^2\left[\epsilon_n^2 + \left(\frac{P_\theta}{m_0 c}\right)^2\right]\right\}^{1/2}\right)^{1/2}. \tag{111}$$

In general, however, the beam is not matched and the beam radius varies along z. As an example, when the magnetic field is zero and the space-charge term ν is negligible compared to the emittance term, the electron beam profile is found to be given by the following solution of (109):

$$r_b(z) = r_b(0)\left[1 + \epsilon^2 z^2/r_b^4(0)\right]^{1/2},$$

where $r_b(0)$ is the electron beam waist at $z = 0$. The profile of a Gaussian radiation beam is given by a similar formula:

$$r_s(z) = r_s(0)\left[1 + \lambda^2 z^2/\pi^2 r_s^4(0)\right]^{1/2},$$

where $r_s(0)$ is the radiation-beam waist, and λ is the radiation wavelength. If we require $r_b = r_s$ to ensure maximum geometrical overlap of the radiation and electron beams, we find the relation

$$\lambda = \pi\epsilon. \tag{112}$$

Note that in Eq. (112) the emittance is assumed to be in units of length and radians. This simple relation between the radiation wavelength and emittance provides an indication of the demands placed on the emittance of the electron beam to obtain good coupling as a result of the geometrical overlap.

There are a number of factors that change this simple picture significantly in realistic cases. For example, the wiggler provides a focusing force that modifies the equilibrium radius of the electron beam.[54,135] In the case of a helical wiggler the beam radius is related to the normalized emittance by $\epsilon_n = \gamma_0 k_\beta r_b^2$, where $k_\beta = |e| B_w / \sqrt{2} \gamma_0 m_0 c^2$ is the betatron wavenumber. Also, the FEL interaction causes a shift in the phase of the radiation beam, resulting in self-focusing of the radiation beam, as discussed in Sec. IV. Thus, in general, the relationship between the radiation wavelength and the electron beam emittance given by Eq. (112) is only indicative of the scaling.

B. Brightness and FEL beam quality

The output power of a FEL is determined by the beam voltage, current, and efficiency. A simple relation between the beam current and emittance was suggested by Neil.[136] This relation, originally known as the Lawson–Penner relation, has the form[85,134]

$$\epsilon_n \,(\text{cm mrad}) = 320\sqrt{I_b[A]}. \tag{113}$$

This formula provides a connection between beam current and emittance, from which the optimum operating conditions for single-pass FEL designs can be determined.[134] However, this relation is based on an empirical scaling of data from linear accelerators and is equivalent to the assumption that all accelerators have the same brightness. It has been pointed out by Roberson[85,138] and others[139,140] that there are many exceptions to this relation. Consequently, brightness of an electron beam has now become a frequently used figure of merit for accelerators used to drive FELs. The normalized brightness is defined by[134]

$$B_n = \alpha_0 I_b / \pi^2 \epsilon_n^2 \,, \tag{114}$$

where I_b is the beam current and α_0 is of order unity. Brightness is the current divided by the volume of a 4-D ellipsoid in transverse phase space and is chosen in analogy to the optical definition. There is some variation of the form factor α_0 in the expression for the brightness. For a beam with a uniform ellipsoidal cross section, $\alpha_0 = 2$.

For a uniform circular cathode of radius r_c the thermal contribution to the normalized emittance is $\epsilon_n = 2r_c$ $(T/m_0 c^2)^{1/2}$. For typical thermionic emitters, the average transverse energy of emitted electrons is 0.1 eV, which gives a lower limit on the emittance of[141]

$$\epsilon_n = 5.0 \times 10^{-6} (I_b / J_b)^{1/2}, \tag{115}$$

where J_b is in amperes per centimeters squared. The corresponding peak brightness is limited to

$$B_n = \gamma_0 I_b / \pi^2 \epsilon_n^2 = 8.2 \times 10^9 J_b, \tag{116}$$

where we have chosen $\alpha_0 = 2$.

The transverse emittance and brightness are useful parameters characterizing electron beams. Emittance filters[98] preserve beam brightness while reducing beam emittance. However, one of the critical electron beam parameters in the FEL interaction is the axial beam energy spread. For example, the relative axial energy spread due to emittance can be written as

$$(\Delta\gamma_z/\gamma_0)_\epsilon = \tfrac{1}{2}(\epsilon_n/r_b)^2(\gamma_z/\gamma_0)^3, \qquad (117)$$

which, when substituted into the formula for brightness, gives

$$B_n = J_b/2\pi(\Delta\gamma_z/\gamma_0)_\epsilon, \qquad (118)$$

where the subscript on the term in parentheses indicates that the axial energy spread comes from the emittance. The axial energy spread due to space-charge potential is

$$(\Delta\gamma_z/\gamma_0)_{sc} = (r_b\omega_b/2c)^2/\gamma_0 = \nu/\gamma_0, \qquad (119)$$

and the contribution due to the wiggler gradients[54] is

$$(\Delta\gamma_z/\gamma_0)_w = (r_b\Omega_w/2c)^2. \qquad (120)$$

For the cold beam approximation to be valid, the sum of these contributions must be small compared to the cold beam intrinsic FEL efficiency derived in Sec. III.

Beam brightness is a measure of beam quality in transverse phase space and hence it is not explicitly related to the FEL interaction. A useful definition of beam quality for FEL's emphasizes the axial energy spread,[85] and is

$$B_Q = J_b/(\Delta\gamma_z/\gamma_0), \qquad (121)$$

where J_b is the current density, $\gamma_z = (1 - \beta_{z0}^2)^{-1/2}$, and $\Delta\gamma_z$ is the spread in the axial energy from all the sources, such as space charge, wiggler gradients, and pitch angle scattering.

The usefulness of the definition in (121) becomes apparent by noting that there are some mechanisms that can contribute to the axial energy spread, but not necessarily to the transverse energy spread. For example, the self-fields of the beam can create a potential that can cause a spread in the axial beam energy without changing the transverse energy spread. Another example is subharmonic bunching in rf accelerators. Subharmonic bunching compresses the beam in the axial direction in order to increase the peak beam current. Since phase space density is conserved, it follows that compression in the axial direction without an increase in the transverse emittance must necessarily result in an axial energy spread.

The various definitions thus far may be put in perspective by considering several accelerators currently being employed in FEL research. Table IV lists the emittance, brightness, FEL beam quality, and other parameters such as voltage, current, radius, and temporal energy spread for some accelerators with magnetic field-free cathodes. Table V lists the parameters for a number of field-immersed accelerators.

Following Eq. (113) we noted that the so-called "Lawson–Penner relation" assumes that all linacs have the same brightness. However, this is not true. This is illustrated in Fig. 15, which is a plot of beam brightness versus current density. There are two lines on the graph, drawn for reference purposes. One line has a slope that is inversely proportional to the current density. With few exceptions the beam brightness in accelerators with magnetic field-free diodes decreases with current density. There are two rf accelerators that use the technique of subharmonic bunching. The brightness in these cases is exceptionally high. Since subharmonic bunching compresses the beam in the axial direction and increases the beam current without an increase in the transverse emittance, the beam brightness can be significantly enhanced in this way.

Table IV — Linear Accelerators, Parameters Taken from Ref. 85

Location Type	Voltage [MV]	Current [A]	Radius [cm]	Emittance [cm-rad]	$\Delta E(t)/E$ [%]	Brightness [A/cm²−rad²]	Beam Quality [A/cm²]
UCSB electrostatic	2.5	1.2	0.3	7.5×10^{-4}	—	2.2×10^5	2.8×10^5
Stanford University rf Linac/Mark III	44	30	0.01	2.5×10^{-4}	—	5×10^7	—
LANL rf Linac	20	250	0.05	1.6×10^{-2}	1	1.0×10^5	1.1×10^6
Boeing rf Linac	150	250	0.1	5×10^{-3}	1.0	1.0×10^6	5.3×10^6
Osaka rf Linac	34	600	0.3ᵃ	6.7×10^{-3}	1.0	2.8×10^6	2.3×10^6
NRL induction linac	0.7	150	0.7	6.2×10^{-2}	2.0	4.0×10^3	1.2×10^4
LLNL (ETA) induction linac	3.5	850	0.8	0.3	1.0	1.1×10^3	1.5×10^3
MIT	2.0	1100	2.5	3.8×10^{-3}	—	7.4×10^4	4.3×10^3
LLNL (ATA) induction linac	45	2000	5ᵇ	4×10^{-2}	—	1.3×10^5	—
Stanford University SCA (recirculator)	115	2.4	—	1.5×10^{-3}	0.02	1.1×10^5	—
LANL photoinjector	1.1	130	—	1.8×10^{-3}	—	4×10^6	—

ᵃ Assumed radius.
ᵇ Estimated.

81

Table V — Field-Immersed Diodes, Parameters Taken from Ref. 85

Location	Voltage [MV]	Current [kA]	Radius [cm]	$<\theta>$ [mrad]	Magnetic Field [kG]	$\omega_b^2/\gamma_0\Omega_0^2$	Brightness [A/cm^{2}rad^2]	Beam Quality [A/cm^2]
NRL	1.35	1.5	0.3	34	15.0	1.3×10^{-2}	1.2×10^5	1.7×10^5
Austin Research Associates	2.1	13	2.2	38	6.6	8.2×10^{-3}	6.6×10^3	5.0×10^3
LANL	3.3	85	1.0[a]	30	87.0	1.5×10^{-2}	2.4×10^6	6×10^5
Columbia University	0.7	0.2	0.25	—	9.5	1.0×10^{-2}	—	1.8×10^5 (5.7×10^4)[b]

[a] Hollow beam.
[b] Includes energy spread due to wiggler gradients.

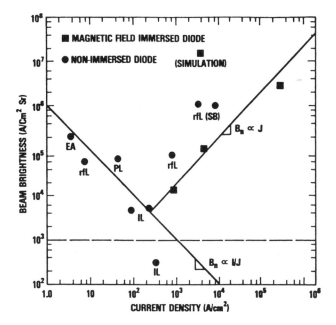

Fig. 15 — Beam brightness vs current density. The dashed line is the value of brightness assumed by the "Lawson-Penner relation" and $\alpha_0 = 1$ was used.

There are three experimental points for the beam brightness of the field-immersed diodes listed in Table V. Note that for these the brightness increases with current density. Another feature is that the angle between the perpendicular and parallel components $\langle \theta \rangle$ listed in Table V is approximately the same for all these experiments. As a result the values of $\Delta\gamma_z/\gamma_0$ for the experiments differ by less than a factor of 3. In other respects the experiments vary widely, for example, the current densities range from 1–400 kA/cm^2. It would appear that the high brightness is due to the high current density.

In Table V the entries for $\omega_b^2/\gamma_0\Omega_0^2$ correspond to the self-field parameter for the field-immersed diodes. It is important to note that although the magnetic fields range from 6.6–87 kG, the value of $\omega_b^2/\gamma_0\Omega_0^2$ is approximately 1% for all the experiments. It should be pointed out that the role of the magnetic field is to prevent space-charge blowup as well as filamentation instabilities.

The term $\epsilon_n^2 + (P_\theta/m_0c)^2$ in Eq. (109) is often treated as an effective transverse emittance in the envelope equation when calculating the radial profile of field-immersed electron beams. That is, both the transverse emittance and the magnetic field determine the waist of the beam. Hence the effective transverse emittance is the relevant quantity in determining the geometrical overlap (filling factor) of the radiation and electron beams.

C. The scaled thermal velocity

Although the beam parameters B_n, ϵ_n, and B_Q are useful figures of merit, a more detailed knowledge of FEL scaling requires the dispersion relation. In Sec. II we discussed the dispersion relation for the FEL in a magnetic field for a cold, monoenergetic beam. In this section we will discuss thermal beam effects. In the high-gain Compton limit and for an electron beam with a Lorentzian electron velocity distribution in an axial magnetic field, this relation has the form[87]

$$D(\omega,k)\left[\omega - v_{z0}(k + k_w) + ikv_{\text{th}}\right]^2$$
$$= \Phi_0 F\omega_b^2\beta_w^2c^2kk_w/\gamma_0, \tag{122}$$

where

$$D(\omega,k) = \omega^2 - c^2k^2 - F\omega_b^2/\gamma_0$$

and v_{th} is the axial thermal velocity. This dispersion relation has a form similar to the dispersion relation for the interaction of an electron beam with a plasma.[86] Following Ref. 86, we find an effective or scaled thermal velocity as

$$S \simeq (v_{th}/v_{z0}) F (4\omega^2 \gamma_0 \gamma_z^2 / \Phi_0 \omega_b^2 \beta_w^2)^{1/3}. \qquad (123)$$

Figure 16 is a plot of the ratio of the beam thermal velocity to the difference between the beam velocity and the phase velocity of the fastest growing ponderomotive wave. When S approaches 1, the phase velocity of the ponderomotive wave approaches the thermal velocity in the beam frame. That is, we make the transition from the cold beam limit to the warm beam, or kinetic regime. This transition causes a change in the topology of the dispersion relation. This was observed in a beam–plasma experiment by Roberson and Gentle.[21] Near resonance, Φ_0 can become large, resulting in a reduction of the phase velocity of the ponderomotive/space-charge wave.

Brightness and FEL beam quality are good figures of merit for accelerator designers without a need for knowledge of specific FEL parameters. However, the output power of a given FEL can be different for the same brightness or beam quality numbers. The scaled thermal velocity provides the simplest next step in characterizing the effect of thermal spread on the FEL interaction. For example, we see from Eq. (123) that S is proportional to the thermal spread but depends on the density to the $-\frac{1}{3}$ power.

The scaled thermal velocity can be expressed in terms of the cold beam efficiency as

$$S = \gamma_z^2 v_{th} / \eta v_{z0}.$$

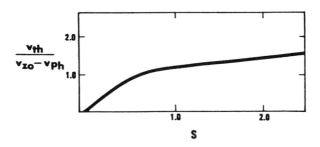

Fig. 16 — Ratio of the difference between the beam velocity and the phase velocity of the ponderomotive wave and the thermal velocity vs scaled thermal velocity

Whereas before we had to require that $\Delta\gamma_z/\gamma_0$ be small compared to the efficiency we now express η in terms of S and the transition to the kinetic regime occurs at $S \simeq 1$.

D. Electron sources

The axial energy spread or effective temperature can come from many sources as electrons emerge from the cathode. These include (i) temperature of the cathode; (ii) roughness of the emitting surface; (iii) nonuniform emission from the cathode surface; (iv) electric and magnetic fields that are asymmetric, nonuniform, or nonadiabatic in the axial direction; and (v) self-fields of the electron beam.

The contribution to the beam emittance due to surface roughness has been considered in detail by Lau.[142] It is found that the maximum value of $\gamma_0\beta_0\langle\theta\rangle$ [cf. Eq. (110)] is expressible as

$$\gamma_0\beta_0\langle\theta\rangle = 0.16\sqrt{E_0}h/(h^2 + w^2)^{1/4},$$

86

in the temperature limited case, and

$$\gamma_0\beta_0\langle\theta\rangle = 0.079\sqrt{E_0}\,[h\,/(h^2 + w^2)^{1/4}]\,(h\,/D)^{1/6},$$

in the space-charge limited case, where E_0 is the average electric field in the anode–cathode gap in mega-electron-volts per centimeter, h is the height of the bump, w is the width in units of 100 μm, and D is the anode–cathode spacing in centimeters. Another interesting case is when the emittance induced by passing a beam through an anode mesh of high transparency, i.e., where the wire dimension is much less than the mesh grid spacing b. In this case[143]

$$\gamma_0\beta_0\langle\theta\rangle = \frac{1}{2\sqrt{6}}\left(\frac{b}{D}\right)\frac{\gamma_0 - 1}{\beta_0}.$$

Plasma cathodes operate by the production of dense, localized plasmas at field enhancement points on the cathode surface. These cathodes are rugged and produce high current densities. However, nonuniformity of plasma production can lead to poor beam quality and plasma expansion into the anode–cathode gap limits the pulse length to a few microseconds.

As experiments have strived to improve the beam quality in plasma cathode diodes, the trend has been away from graphite brush and mesh cathode,[96,144-146] which give low turn-on voltages and closure velocities, to smoother surfaces, such as velvet. Bekefi et al.[147] have carried out beam emittance and brightness measurements in both graphite and velvet cathodes using pulse-line driven, field-free diodes. The results are shown in Fig. 17. Here $\delta\theta$ is the beam divergence angle that is about a factor of 1.5 to 2 better than reported in the three field-immersed pulse-line diode experiments listed in Table V. It appears then that in four separate

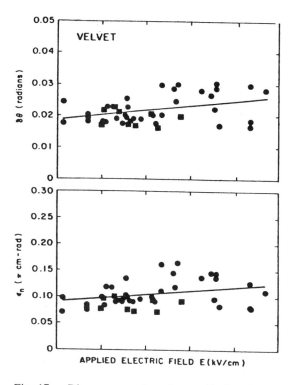

Fig. 17 — Divergence angle and normalized emittance vs
applied electric field for a velvet cathode

time integrated experiments the measured value of $\langle \theta \rangle$ is
approximately 30 mrad.

Bekefi *et al.*[148] have made temporal measurements of the
evolution of beam emittance from a field emission electron
gun. They found the average beam divergence angle associated with velvet cathodes to be about a factor of 4 better
than with graphite at early times (< 2 nsec). Initially $\delta\theta$ for
velvet is 4 mrad, in close agreement with Lau's[142] estimate of
the spread due to only surface roughness. At late times

88

(> 30 nsec), however, the divergence angle for both graphite and velvet cathodes approach 4 mrad.

The FEL mechanism is sensitive to temporal variations in the energy of the driving beam. Changes in the beam energy can shift the FEL out of the mode to which it is tuned. In rf linacs the time variations of the beam energy in rf linacs are related to the Q of the cavity.[85] The FEL is also sensitive to low frequency noise in the accelerator.[149] Temporal variations in the recirculating electrostatic accelerator are primarily due to variations in the charging rate as a result of beam current losses.[150] Temporal variations in pulse-line accelerators and induction linacs are partially due to pulse forming networks and core losses.

Plasma–cathode diodes have a time-dependent voltage that results from the expansion of the plasma into the anode–cathode gap. The anode–cathode closure velocities are typically 0.5–2 cm/μsec, but may be as high as 10 cm/μsec for flashboard cathodes.[140] If we assume the effective diode spacing d decreases as $d = d_0 - vt$, where d_0 is the initial anode–cathode spacing and v is the closure velocity, then the diode voltage variation as a function of time[96] is given by $V_D(t) = V_D(0)d/d_0$, where V_D is the initial diode voltage. Using the Langmuir–Child law, the beam current is given by

$$I = APV_D^{3/2}/d^2 = APV_{D0}^{3/2}/d_0^{3/2}(d_0 - vt)^{1/2},$$

where A is the cathode area and P is the perveance. Hence beam current increases and beam voltage decreases as a function of time during the pulse. For example, if we consider the ATA injector at LLNL,[140] where $d_0 = 2.9$ cm, $v \simeq 10$ cm/μsec, we find an increase in the beam current of $\sim 40\%$ in 150 nsec. Humphries et al.[151] have reported a grid-controlled plasma cathode that has the potential of solving the anode–cathode closure problem at modest current densities ($2–20$ A/cm^2).

Free-electron lasers require high quality, high current density, and high average power electron beams. These beam requirements have revived interest in thermionic cathodes[140] and photocathodes.[141] Barium oxide thermionic cathodes are usually limited to current densities of less than 5 A/cm^2, require high vacuum, and are susceptible to poisoning. Dispenser cathodes produce current densities of 30 A/cm^2 and controlled porosity dispenser cathodes may generate as much as 100 A/cm^2. Lanthanum hexaboride cathodes[152–154] can be operated in excess of 100 A/cm^2 and are rugged but require high operating temperatures that shorten the lifetime.[155]

Laser driven photocathodes have received considerable attention. These cathodes have the potential to provide high current density as well as synchronizing the beam micropulses with the accelerating wave in rf linacs. Oettinger et al.[156] have reported results from a Cs$_3$Sb photocathode using a frequency doubled Nd-glass laser. A current of 80 A was emitted from a 1 cm^2 surface for 50 nsec. Measured normalized emittances were between 5 and 9π mm mrad, with a normalized peak brightness of 10^{11} A/m^2 rad^2. Experiments at LANL have been carried out to accelerate a beam from a photocathode with minimum degradation in the energy.[141] The normalized emittance for peak currents of 130 A was 20π mm mrad. The normalized peak brightness was 4×10^{10} A/cm^2 rad^2 with an average macropulse current of 1.0 A, and an energy of 1.1 MeV.

Westenskow and Madey[157] have reported a novel microwave gun used to inject micropulses into a rf linac driven FEL. The gun uses a Lanthanum hexaboride cathode and is driven by the same klystron that is used to drive the rf linac. They reported a normalized brightness of 10^6 A/cm^2 rad^2 and a peak current of 20 A.[158] The brightness in these experiments was comparable with the result obtained by subharmonic bunching.

VII. EXPERIMENTS

The past ten years have seen many FEL "proof-of-principle" experiments in which the wavelength ranged from centimeters to submicrons and the powers from gigawatts to less than milliwatts. These experiments can be characterized by the kind of accelerator used to drive the FEL. For example, the pulse-line diode is a high current, $\geqslant$ kA, low voltage, ~ 1 MeV, beam generator. When used as an injector for an induction linac it can become a high current, $\gtrsim$ kA, high voltage, ~ 50 MeV, accelerator. The rf linac is a high voltage, $\gtrsim 100$ MeV, low average current, < 1 A, accelerator that is capable of producing peak currents as high as a kiloampere for pulse durations of ~ 10 psec. The storage ring is a high voltage, > 100 MeV, low average current, ~ 0.1 mA, device. Finally, the electrostatic accelerator is a moderate voltage, < 20 MeV, low current device, with ~ 1 A recirculating current.

One of the distinguishing characteristics of these accelerators is the pulse length of the electron beam. The electrostatic accelerator has been used to operate a FEL with pulse times from 5–30 μsec, induction linacs from 40 nsec to 2 μsec, and pulse-line accelerators from 20–200 nsec. These accelerators are usually run single pulse, or at low repetition rates. Radio frequency linacs have micropulses that are a few picoseconds long, but have pulse trains (macropulses) that

91

are from a few microseconds to milliseconds and under limited conditions, can be operated continuously. The storage ring has micropulse lengths of about a nanosecond that can remain in the ring for more than an hour.

In this section we will review some of the proof-of-principle FEL experiments, driven by each of these accelerator types. These experiments demonstrate the FEL's tunability, high power, and wide range of wavelength capability, making it a candidate for many applications. The interest in FEL research with its requirements of high beam currents and high beam quality has stimulated research in new accelerators. Figure 18 shows the different wavelength ranges in which various types of accelerators have been used to drive free-electron lasers and the wavelength regime over which they may be scaled.

One of the earliest amplifiers based on the idea of an electron beam propagating through a magnetic wiggler field was built by Phillips at the GE Microwave Laboratory in 1957. This low-voltage device, called a ubitron, initially operated in the X band. Subsequent tubes were developed that operated in the S-band region. The S-band tubes, developed in 1960, had a small-signal gain of 13 dB at 135 kV, a saturation power of 1.2 MW, and an efficiency of 10%. Experiments indicating the possibility of efficiency enhancement by spatially tapering the wiggler field were also performed but not reported. The advent of the modern FEL was initiated in 1971 by Madey's calculation of the gain and subsequent experiments in the infrared region using the Stanford superconducting linac.[10,11]

The following is a review of some of the key FEL experiments. These include experiments employing axial guide magnetic fields and FEL's driven by induction accelerators, rf linacs, electrostatic accelerators, and storage rings.

92

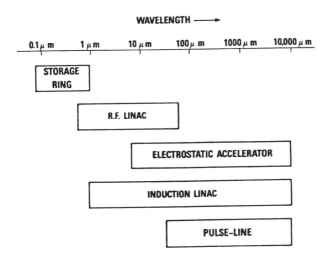

Fig. 18 — Typical accelerators used to drive free-electron lasers

A. Free-electron lasers in an axial guiding magnetic field

Experiments on FEL's in a combined wiggler and axial magnetic field have concentrated on microwave frequencies. This work was performed primarily at NRL, Columbia University, Yale University, MIT, Hebrew University, École Polytechnique,[159] UCLA, and Hughes Research Laboratory.

In an early paper, Sprangle et al.[30,82] pointed out the possibility of gain enhancement near cyclotron resonance in a collective FEL immersed in a magnetic field. Since then the theory has evolved to include many effects unique to the field-immersed FEL. We will review the work at several institutions and discuss some of the key experiments in detail.

Experiments at Columbia University using a pulse-line accelerator in field-immersed free-electron lasers were begun by Efthimion and Schlesinger,[160] Marshall et al., [161] and

93

Gilgenbach et al.[162] In a joint experiment between NRL and Columbia University, several megawatts of power at a wavelength of 400 μm were observed.[163] These FEL oscillator experiments were carried out at NRL using a 1.2 MeV, 25 kA, 50 nsec beam. Strong radiation at a wavelength of 400 μm and a narrowing of the radiation pulse were observed when the mirrors were aligned, but only low-level superradiance, i.e., growth from noise, was obtained when the optical system was misaligned.

Experiments at the Hebrew University have verified the calculations of the transition from helical to nonhelical orbits[83] and demonstrated the necessity for adiabatic transitions in the wiggler amplitude.[164]

The low efficiency of the NRL–Columbia experiment,[163] 0.003%, focused subsequent efforts on improving the electron beam quality. In these high current and low energy beams the energy spread is dominated by space-charge effects.

By selecting the central part of the beam and tapering the anode to minimize perturbations, the relative axial energy spread due to perturbations was reduced to less than a percent.[165] In addition, the reduction in the beam current to 1.5 kA resulted in a 2.5% axial energy spread because of space charge.

Further experiments at NRL were carried out using the improved diode design. The experiment[92] was operated as a super-radiant amplifier. The radiated power as a function of axial guide field B_0 is shown in Fig. 19. The onset of measurable power at low guide fields was due to the increase in transmitted beam current with increasing B_0. The drop in radiation power at $B_0 = 10$ kG was consistent with the transition from Group I to Group II orbits. Above gyroreso-

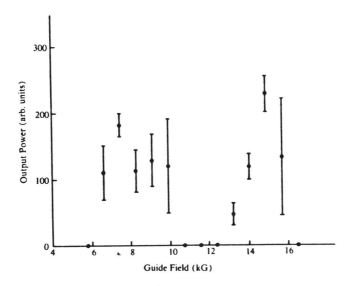

Fig. 19 — Measured variation in the FEL output power ($\lambda > 5$ mm) for a magnetic field immersed diode. The beam voltage was 1.35 MV, and current 1.5 kA. The wiggler period was 3 cm, the radial component of the wiggler field was 0.63 kG and the beam radius was 3 mm. The peak output power was 35 MW.

nance, $B_0 = 11.5$ kG, the radiation power was consistent with the interaction with Group II orbits. Measurements indicated peak powers of 35 MW at a wavelength of 4 mm with an efficiency of 2.5%.

Additional super-radiant experiments carried out at NRL by Gold et al.[166,167] concentrated on operation above gyroresonance where the coupling parameter Φ_0 was less than zero. Improvements in efficiency resulted in the generation of 75 MW at a wavelength of 4 mm. When the output radiation was focused, air breakdown at atmospheric pressure was achieved. The power and wavelength could be estimated by a technique developed by Mako et al.[168]

Amplifier experiments at NRL operated at a wavelength of 8.6 mm. Total linear gains in excess of 50 dB, at a spatial growth rate of 1.2 dB/cm, resulted in 17 MW at an efficiency in excess of 3% (Ref. 169). In 1980, the group at the École Polytechnique, using a field emission electron beam observed emission from 50–300 GHz in a FEL experiment employing an axial magnetic field.[170] The broad output spectrum was obtained when the axial magnetic field was tuned to approximately the cyclotron resonance. The total power generated over the full spectrum was ~ 2.5 MW. In a more recent series of experiments at the École Polytechnique,[171] a Raman FEL operated at ~20% efficiencies was reported. In these experiments, the small diameter electron beam (1–6 mm) had a current ranging from 30–300 A at a voltage of 600 kV. With an axial magnetic field of 10 kG they observed a gain of 3 dB/cm.

Figure 20 is a sketch of the Columbia University experiment employing the Thomson backscattering diagnostic for beam quality measurements.[93] Measurements of beam quality are critical to the understanding and improvement of the free-electron laser. Thomson scattering is a diagnostic tool that can determine both the relative beam energy spread and beam density. These measurements include both the space-charge and wiggler contributions to the energy spread. Only 10% of the beam was extracted through a 5 mm diameter aperture. The beam current density was approximately 1 kA/cm^2. Thomson scattering at relatively low beam densities ($\simeq 10^{11}$ cm^{-3}) becomes a viable diagnostic for beam quality measurements, because at relativistic energies there

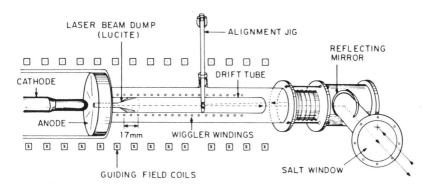

Fig. 20 — Experimental configuration for Thomson backscattering measurements of beam quality in a FEL. The anode was a graphite disk with a 15° conical concave surface and a 5 mm aperture on axis. The cold cathode, made from graphite, was separated from the anode by a 15 mm gap and the entire beam was immersed in a uniform guiding field of 9.5 kG. The apertured beam propagates along the axis of a 71 cm long, 1.9 cm i.d. stainless steel drift tube.

is an enhancement in the effective scattering cross section in the electron beam direction. The disadvantage of this measurement is poor spatial resolution since the entire length of the electron beam is observed.

The incident radiation wavelength from the CO_2 laser used in the Thomson scattering experiment was at 9.6 μm. The spectrum was obtained by filtering the scattered radiation with a set of narrow band interference filters, having transmission peaks located at $\frac{1}{2}$ μm with bandwidths of 50, 80, 100, 250, and 500 Å. Figure 21 shows the energy spread measured in the experiment as a function of β_w^2, where β_w is the normalized wiggle velocity. At $\beta_w = 0$ the energy spread is approximately 0.5%, which is expected from the space charge of the beam. At high values of β_w the measured values approach the calculated values as a result of the wiggler.

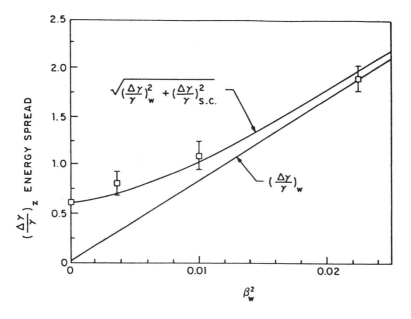

Fig. 21 — Dependence of the axial parallel energy spread on the wiggle velocity. The straight line is a calculation of the expected inhomogenous broadening due to the undulator. The curved line is due to undulator and self-potential of the beam resulting from space charge. The contribution from the diode emittance is negligible.

Thomson scattering is potentially an ideal beam quality diagnostic. However, it is extremely difficult to implement.

Masud *et al.*[70,71] have reported a super-radiant 2 mm FEL with an output power of 2 MW and observations of sidebands on the power spectrum. The Columbia University group has reported high power (12 MW) radiation pulses (100 nsec) at a wavelength of 2.5 mm. In the experiment, the tapered section improved the efficiency from 3% to 12%. In addition, they found that the tapered wiggler produced much less sideband radiation than the constant period wiggler.[72] Cai *et al.*[94] have carried out experiments at Columbia University in which optical guiding effects were reported.

In a field-immersed FEL experiment carried out at MIT by Fajans *et al.*[95] measurements were compared with the theory and computer simulations.[130] A mildly relativistic electron beam, 175 kV, at low currents, 1–8 A, was used to generate radiation. Continuous, single mode tuning from 7 to 21 GHz was demonstrated. Over 100 kW of power at an efficiency of 12% and a maximum gain of 20 dB were reported in the amplifier mode. The electron beam was generated by a thermionically emitting Pierce-type electron gun. In contrast to a diode immersed in an axial magnetic field, as in the case of the NRL and Columbia University experiments, electrostatic focusing was used. An assembly of six focusing coils was designed so that the magnetic field was along the zero-magnetic-field electron trajectories. The beam was compressed and apertured to a radius of 0.25 cm, resulting in a beam current density of about 50 A/cm^2. The fractional axial energy spread due to emittance was measured to be 0.3%. A 2 m long, 2.54 cm diameter drift tube acted as a cylindrical waveguide, whose fundamental TE_{11} mode had a cutoff frequency of 6.92 GHz.

Measurements of gain as a function of wiggler strength under conditions of constant input frequency, beam current, and axial guide field are shown in Fig. 22. These measurements represent a good test of the theoretical model.

By varying the injected input frequency and measuring the voltage at which amplification occurred, the frequency-voltage characteristics of the FEL were determined. The results are shown in Fig. 23. The frequency can be tuned continuously by a factor of 3. Gain was readily observed for both

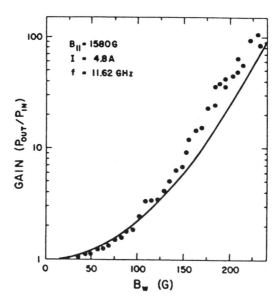

Fig. 22 — Comparison of measured and calculated gain vs wiggler strength.

the low- and high-frequency branches of the FEL instability, and for low and high values of the guide magnetic field.

The FEL frequency characteristics were studied near resonance by determining the beam energy necessary to amplify a 12.33 GHz signal as a function of the axial magnetic field; the results are shown in Fig. 24. Slightly above resonance spontaneous oscillations precluded amplifier operation and the FEL was run as an oscillator. Well below resonance the required energy was approximately constant, but increased sharply near resonance. Similarly, above resonance the required beam energy was virtually constant until the axial magnetic field was lowered into the resonant region. The vertical data lines in the resonance region indicate

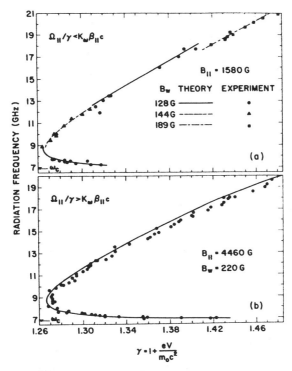

Fig. 23 — Radiation frequency as a function of beam voltage for an FEL amplifier. The results are plotted for both group I ($\Omega_{11}/\gamma < k_w\beta_{11}c$) and above resonance ($\Omega_{11}/\gamma < k_w\beta_{11}c$) where $\Omega_{11}/\gamma = \Omega_0$ and $\beta_{11} = \beta_{z0}$. The horizontal arrows denote the cutoff frequency of the TE_{11} mode.

where the magnetic coupling parameter Φ_0 is less than zero. The fact that the frequency can be tuned over a broad range of electron energies implies a broad bandwidth as predicted by theory. In the presence of a guide magnetic field the cyclotron maser instability may well be excited and compete with the FEL instability.[96,172]

Below gyroresonance (Group I orbits) the ponderomotive/space-charge wave couples directly to a waveguide

101

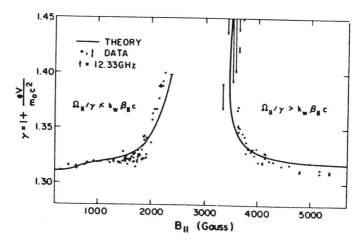

Fig. 24 — Beam energy required for radiation at $f = 12.33$ GHz as a function of axial magnetic field both far from and near resonance. The solid lines are from the theory. The long vertical lines signify broad band operation.

mode. Above gyroresonance (Group II orbits) the pondero-motive/space-charge wave couples the cyclotron body mode of the beam to a waveguide mode.[84] Just above resonance, the magnetic coupling parameter Φ_0 is negative, resulting in a ponderomotive/space-charge wave that is unstable to a "negative mass type" of instability. This instability results in large growth rates. Computer simulations have shown the region where $\Phi_0 < 0$ is the least sensitive to beam quality requirements and has large growth rates. This is consistent with the experimental results of Gold et al.[166,167] who observed the largest power levels in the region $\Phi_0 < 0$ and Fajans et al.[95] who found the gain was too high to operate as an amplifier in this region.

Fajans et al. and Orzechowski et al.[173] have reported measurements of the rf phase in both the linear and nonlinear regimes. These phase shifts are relevant to the phenomena of optical guiding, which is capable of extending the FEL interaction length beyond that allowed by the Rayleigh diffraction limit.

An alternative to increasing the beam voltage to obtain short wavelength radiation is to decrease the period. As a result of technical difficulties in the precision machining of wigglers with periods less than a few centimeters, there have been several studies of the use of microwigglers and of electromagnetic waves as wigglers. The radiation from an electron beam propagating antiparallel to an electromagnetic wave is essentially equivalent to that from an electron beam traveling through a wiggler field. The equivalent wiggler magnetic field is $B_w[\text{kG}] = 2.3 \ (P[\text{GW}]/\sigma[\text{cm}^2])^{1/2}$, where σ is the cross-sectional area, and the power P of the electromagnetic wave. For example, a CO_2 laser at 10 μm can produce 10^{13} W. In backward wave oscillator experiments, using intense relativistic electron beams, high power microwaves at wavelengths of several centimeters can be generated. Carmel et al.[174] designed a two-stage FEL using a 500 MW, 12.5 GHz backward wave oscillator as an electromagnetic wiggler. They reported high-frequency radiation at 140 GHz. Danly et al.[175] have suggested gyrotrons may also make good electromagnetic wigglers for FEL's.

B. Free-electron lasers driven by induction linacs

An induction accelerating module can be thought of as a pulse transformer in which the electron beam forms part of the secondary. Since the accelerating electric field is inductive, modules may be added consecutively to obtain higher electron beam energies. A schematic of a section of an induction linac is shown in Fig. 25.

103

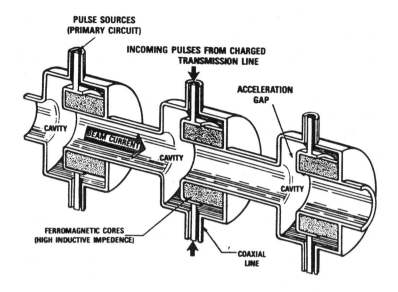

Fig. 25 — Induction accelerator modules connected in series

Induction linacs can produce high current, high energy electron beams with pulse durations ranging from nanoseconds to microseconds. The distinct advantage of the induction linac is its high peak power capability. A drawback of this type of accelerator for FEL's is its relatively poor beam quality.

The first FEL experiment using an induction linac accelerator (ILA) was carried out at NRL by Roberson et al.[96] Figure 26 is a diagram of the long pulse induction linac used in this experiment. The two microsecond pulse length made this device unique among induction linear accelerators.[176] The accelerator consisted of two major components: an injector and an induction module. The electron gun in the injector section had a large tungsten dispenser thermionic cathode (16.5 cm diam). Electrons were accelerated in the

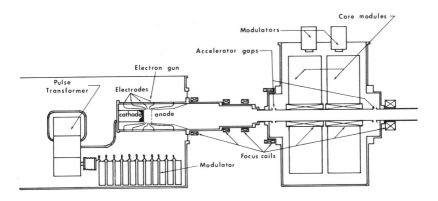

Fig. 26 — Schematic diagram of the long pulse linear induction accelerator. The accelerator consisted of an injector and a 2 μs induction module.

gun through a series of 12 annular electrodes, separated by ceramic insulator rings. The last electrode supported a 95% transmission tungsten mesh at ground potential.

With a dispenser cathode, the voltage remained constant to within a few percent over the full 2 μsec pulse length. Because of the difficulties in obtaining and maintaining a large area dispenser cathode in the vacuum conditions of the accelerator, a "graphite brush cathode" was used instead.[145,146] The graphite cathode was mounted on the same cathode stock as the thermionic cathode and generally produces a relatively flat current waveform with fast turn-on and minimal impedance collapse.[144] However, the electron beam's emittance was about twice are high as with the dispenser cathode.

Beam transport was found to be quite sensitive to the type of cathode used. Focusing fields had to be changed considerably from those used with the dispenser cathode. Figure

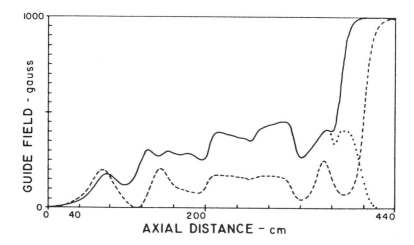

Fig. 27 — Magnetic focusing field profiles in the long pulse linear induction accelerator. The dashed curve is the field for the thermionic cathode. The solid curve is the field optimized for the graphite brush cathode. Without the 1 kG guiding field, the field drops to zero as shown by the dotted line.

27 shows the magnetic field profile needed for beam transport for the thermionic and for the graphite brush cathodes. Computer simulations[177] and envelope equation calculations were carried out to model and optimize the beam transport.

Initial experiments were conducted with the wiggler immersed in an axial guide magnetic field. In these experiments, the cathode was in a field-free region. This configuration has the potential advantage that electron beams with a Brillouin flow equilibrium may, in certain cases, be established, thereby eliminating axial energy spread due to space charge. However, the transport into the solenoidal field produced a large spread in the axial component of energy.[96] This

106

energy spread was primarily a result of conservation of canonical angular momentum in a configuration where the electrons traversed a field-free region in the diode before entering the wiggler that was immersed in the axial magnetic field. The current in this experiment was not sufficiently high to establish Brillouin flow.

A careful parameter study was carried out using a diffuse wiggler to identify which of the observed radiation frequencies were due to the FEL interaction and which were due to the cyclotron interaction.[96] Both modes were present, but most of the power resulted from the low-frequency electron cyclotron–beam interaction. The FEL frequency was 11.7 GHz and the power approximately 10 kW.

The solenoidal magnetic field in the FEL interaction region leads to complications. This was not only because of the problems arising from additional beam modes in the system, but a large azimuthal component of velocity was imparted to the beam in going from the magnetic field-free diode into the solenoidal magnetic field. The transition from the accelerator to the solenoidal magnetic field resulted in a large energy spread in the axial beam energy because the beam density was too low for Brillouin flow.

The axial magnetic field was turned off and the linac transport system extended to inject the beam directly into a helical wiggler without a guide field. Radiation diagnostics included high-pass filters, crystal detectors, and a gas breakdown spectrometer.[168] Since there was no axial guide field, the wiggler provided all the electron beam focusing. The transported beam current was approximately 200 A. The radiation power spectrum is shown in Fig. 28. The horizontal bars represent the step sizes of the cutoff filters used to

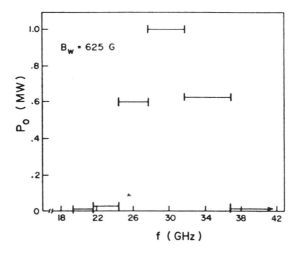

Fig. 28 — Power spectrum with a helical wiggler and no guide field.
The amplitude of the wiggler field is 625 G.

obtain the spectrum. The emission peaked at a frequency of
~ 30 GHz with radiated powers in excess of 1 MW.[144]

Improvements in the beam transport and suppression of
low-frequency oscillations (550 MHz) resulted in peak
powers of 4 MW with a corresponding efficiency of 3%.[97,178]
In addition to the 30 GHz radiation, approximately 100 kW
of radiation at 7 GHz was measured. The observed frequency corresponded to a backward wave FEL mode.

In summary, when the axial field was eliminated and the
beam injected directly into the helical wiggler, a dramatic
improvement in both the power and spectral purity was observed. Radiated power levels of 4 MW at 30 GHz were
measured with a beam current of ~ 200 A, corresponding to
an intrinsic efficiency of 3%.

Induction linac technology has been extensively developed at LLNL.[179] The Experimental Test Accelerator

(ETA)[180] produced a 10 kA electron beam with a peak energy of 4.5 MeV and a pulse duration of 30 nsec. The Advanced Test Accelerator (ATA) produced a 10 kA electron beam with a peak energy of 50 MeV and a pulse duration of 70 nsec.[181] Both machines typically run at a repetition rate of one pulse per second.

In experiments at LLNL a 500 A, 3.3 MeV beam from the ETA was used in a FEL experiment at microwave frequencies.[98] A linear wiggler magnetic field was generated by two series of rectangular solenoids. Each two periods of the wiggler were energized by their own independently controlled power supply. This provided flexibility in adjusting the amplitude of the wiggler to enhance the radiation efficiency. The small axial field above and below the wiggler plane provided for vertical focusing of the electron beam; however, additional focusing had to be applied in the wiggler plane. A horizontally focusing quadrupole field with a gradient of 30 G/cm was applied on the wiggler plane to stabilize the beam. A sketch of the apparatus is shown in Fig. 29.

Figure 30 is a plot of the output power versus distance when the input signal was sufficiently large that nonlinear saturation occurs in the length of the system. The solid points are the experimental results. The open circles are the results of 2-D simulations. Before saturation, the output

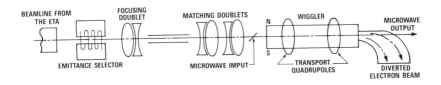

Fig. 29 — A sketch of the experimental test accelerator (ETA)
FEL apparatus

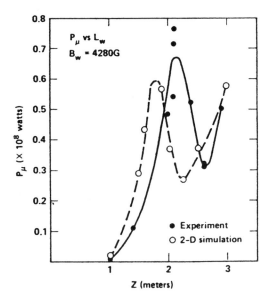

Fig. 30 — Power as a function of wiggler length in the LLNL FEL experiment. The solid dots are experimental points, the open circles result from two-dimensional calculations. The beam voltage was 3.3 MV, current 500 A, radiation frequency 34.6 GHz and the output power was 80 MW.

power as a function of wiggler length shows an exponential gain of approximately 15.6 dB/m. The small-signal gain was measured to be 13.4 dB/m. The peak power is approximately 80 MW. Hence the efficiency is approximately 5%. The oscillations in the output power are a clear indication of the beam particles trapped in the ponderomotive/space-charge wave. The wavelength of these trapped-particle oscillations[43] (synchrotron oscillations) is

$$\lambda_s = 2\pi (\gamma_0 m_0^2 c^3 / |e|^2 E_s B_w)^{1/2},$$

110

where E_s is the peak electric field of the radiation. The observed wavelength of the oscillations was 25% longer than calculated.[99] This is attributed, in part, to longitudinal space-charge effects.

A wavelength 40% longer than that calculated for particles trapped at the bottom of the potential well was observed in the nonlinear saturation of the two stream instability by Gentle and Roberson.[22] The conclusion in that case was that the beam particles were trapped one-fourth of the way from the top of the potential well. In general, the period (in the wave frame) depends on the amplitude of oscillation in the potential well (as in a large amplitude pendulum). The result is a longer oscillation wavelength in the laboratory frame.

One of the advantages of the wiggler design in the Livermore experiment is the flexibility in adjusting the amplitude of the wiggler. This can be used to enhance nonlinearly the radiation efficiency by tapering the amplitude of the wiggler after the beam particles are trapped in the ponderomotive well, hence converting beam kinetic energy to radiation.

The experiment was improved by increasing the current (from 500 to 850 A) and increasing the beam brightness by a factor of two.[99] This resulted in a slight increase in the efficiency (from 5% to 6 %). The injected beam power was 30 kW and the output radiation power 180 MW.

Simulations indicated that the performance of the FEL was quite insensitive to beam emittance. The operating point was where the reduction in gain from space charge and emittance were approximately equal. Hence the rate of change of the gain with emittance was less sensitive because of the additional contribution of space charge. This emphasizes the

111

need for including space-charge contributions in the beam quality (cf. Sec. VI).

A dramatic increase in efficiency was then achieved by tapering the wiggler amplitude beyond the saturation point. In this case, the efficiency was increased from 6% to 34% and the output power was 1 GW. The results of the experiment and numerical simulations are shown in Fig. 31. Both the untapered and tapered wiggler results are shown. The simulations indicate that 75% of the electron beam was trapped and reduced in energy by 45%.

Multimode nonlinear simulations[182] of this experiment have also tested the impact of beam thermal spread on the tapered wiggler interaction. Results indicate that the tapered wiggler tends to reduce the sensitivity of the interaction to

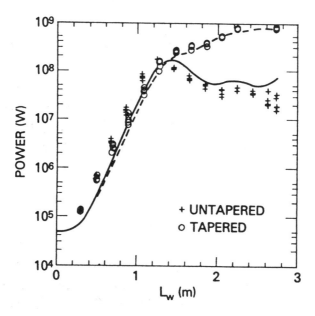

Fig. 31 — Output power of the ETA FEL with tapered wiggler and untapered wiggler

112

beam thermal spread, thereby easing the beam quality requirement.

Free-electron laser experiments operating at 140 GHz were carried out at LLNL using the ETA accelerator.[183] The accelerator and wiggler configuration were unchanged from operation at 35 GHz. The wiggler was operated at a nominal field strength of 1.7 kG, reduced from the 3.7 kG value used at 35 GHz, to satisfy the FEL resonance condition.

With 30 W of input signal, an exponential gain of 21 dB/m and a saturated output power of over 50 MW were measured with an efficiency of 1.8%. Experimental efforts to increase the efficiency by tapering the wiggler amplitude were of limited success.

Simulations indicated that the observed inability to increase power by tapering was due to space-charge and emittance effects. Simulations and measurements at 35 GHz indicate a trapping fraction of about 70% while the tapered simulations at 140 GHz indicate a trapping fraction of less than 30%. The FEL electron beam quality demands at 140 GHz are greater than at 35 GHz.

Free-electron laser experiments operating at 10 μm using the ATA accelerator have been reported.[184,185] The electron beam energy was 45 MeV and the current 700 A. A gain of 27 dB in a 15 m wiggler was measured. With a 14 kW input power, an output power of 7 MW was measured. When the input power was increased to 5 MW, the output power was 50 MW with an efficiency of 0.16% (Ref. 185). Measurements of the radiation spot size indicated gain guiding. With an 8 mm input, the output spot size at the end of the 15 m wiggler, three Rayleigh ranges away, was only 10 mm (Ref. 185).

Induction linac driven FEL experiments are underway in Japan.[186] Preliminary experiments with a 2 MeV and 1 kA electron beam have produced 30 kW at 1 mm wavelength.[187]

C. Free-electron lasers driven by rf linacs

The current interest in short wavelength ($\lambda \ll 1$ mm) FEL's is due in large part to the pioneering work at Stanford University. A series of FEL experiments at infrared wavelengths using the Stanford superconducting rf linac were performed.[9-11]

A rf linac uses a series of resonant cavities at microwave frequencies. Both traveling wave and standing-wave linacs operate by designing the structure to make the phase velocity of the wave nearly equal to the velocity of light. Bunches of electrons are injected on the crest of the forward going wave and accelerated through the entire length of the system. The most widely used electron linac design, the traveling wave linac, was pioneered at Stanford University in the late 1940s. A continuous electron beam, injected into the accelerator, has stable orbits only on a small part of the phase of the accelerating wave. Hence the accelerated beam is bunched into "micropulses" with a duration that is a small fraction of the rf phase. The micropulses are repeated at multiples of the rf period. A long train of micropulses form the macropulse. The pulse timing sequence[188] is shown in Fig. 32. This figure refers to the rf linac FEL experiment at Boeing Aerospace Company. In this case only 1 out of every 36 rf wave periods, or "buckets," are filled.

A FEL amplifier experiment at a wavelength of 10.6 μm was carried out with the Stanford superconducting rf linear accelerator.[10] The superconducting helical wiggler was 5.2 m long and had a period of 3.2 cm. A CO_2 laser was used as

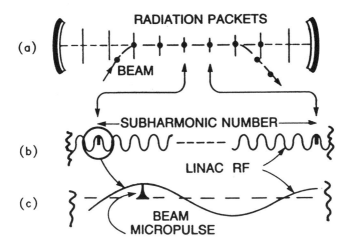

Fig. 32 — Pulse timing sequence shows the time scale from macropulse to micropulse (values refer to the Boeing Aerospace linac): (a) schematic of FEL resonator mirrors, showing synchronization between radiation packets and beam micropulses. Effective mirror one-way transit time 221 ns; (b) beam micropulses occupy a maximum of 1 out of every 36 rf "buckets" for a spacing of 27.7 ns and (c) beam micropulse duration ~20 ps. The linac rf frequency is 1.3 GHz and the macropulse repetition rate is 1 Hz.

the input signal. Figure 33 shows the spontaneous radiation and the stimulated gain as a function of the electron beam energy. At low beam energies, the phase velocity of the ponderomotive wave is greater than the beam velocity and the gain is therefore negative. At high beam energies, the reverse is true and the gain is positive. The peak measured gain was 7% at a peak current of 70 mA. The radiation was circularly polarized as expected for a helical wiggler. The magnitude of the gain was shown to be linearly proportional to beam current from 5 to 70 mA. An analysis of the startup of FEL

115

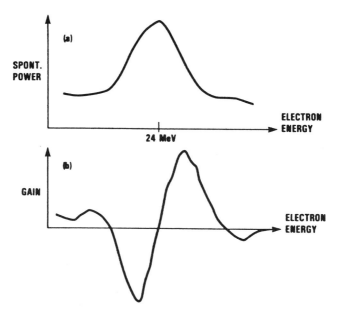

Fig. 33 — The spontaneous radiation and stimulated gain as a function of the electron beam energy. (a) The spontaneous power at 10.6 μm as a function of the electron energy in the first Stanford University FEL amplifier. (b) The amplitude and phase of the modulation imposed on the optical radiation from a CO_2 laser. Amplification corresponds to a positive gain. The electron energy was swept through a small range near resonance at 24 MeV. The helical wiggler field was 2.4 KG and the gain was 7%/pass.

oscillators[189] was applied to this experiment and shown to be in good agreement with observations.

Following the amplifier experiment, the Stanford group reported operation of an FEL oscillator experiment[11] at 3.4 μm. The peak output power was approximately 7 kW and the average power was 0.36 W. The intracavity (circulating) power was 500 kW. Figure 34(a) shows the spectrum above

116

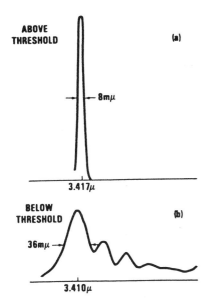

ABOVE THRESHOLD

(a)

8mμ

3.417μ

BELOW THRESHOLD

(b)

36mμ

3.410μ

Fig. 34 — Spectra above and below threshold, (a) Emission spectrum above threshold in the first Stanford University FEL oscillator experiment. The wavelength is 3.41 μm. (b) Spontaneous radiation emitted by the electron beam. The stimulated radiation was more than seven orders of magnitude greater than the spontaneous radiation.

threshold where the peak power was 7 kW. Figure 34(b) shows the spontaneous spectrum below threshold where the peak power was 0.1 mW. The laser line width was 8 nm (200 GHz) and the efficiency was 0.006%.

At EG&G, Inc., Santa Barbara, the TRW group carried out an experiment using a variable wiggler.[190] The wiggler field had a constant period but varied in amplitude along the beam axis. The spontaneous spectrum and the electron beam energy loss due to the FEL interaction were measured and compared with theory. With 2.25% magnetic field taper, 12% of the electrons were decelerated by 0.6%. The corresponding gain was 2.7% and the efficiency was 0.07%. This result was an order of magnitude higher than that calculated for an untapered wiggler. The TRW group has reported operation of a tapered wiggler, free-electron laser oscillator experiment using the Stanford Superconducting Accelerator.[191,192] In this experiment the FEL operated at 1.6 μm, with a peak power of 1.3 MW and extraction efficiency as high as 1.2%.

The first rf linac driven FEL experiment in the visible regime was carried out by the TRW–Stanford group.[193] The electron beam energy was doubled by recirculating it through the rf linac. Peak electron beam currents of 2.4 A at 115 MeV, produced 21 kW of power at 0.52 μm. The small-signal gain in this experiment was 0.2% per ampere, which was an order of magnitude lower than the theoretical value of 3% per ampere.

A FEL amplifier experiment was carried out at Los Alamos National Laboratory (LANL) using a high power (50–900 MW) CO_2 laser and a rf linac.[194] With an input signal of 750 MW, more than 50% of the electrons were trapped by the ponderomotive wave and decelerated. Using an electron spectrometer the energy lost by the beam as a result of the FEL interaction was measured and the efficiency determined. The maximum extraction efficiency occurred at a beam energy of 20.8 MeV. At energies less than about 20.5 MeV the electrons are accelerated.

The LANL group also has carried out a FEL oscillator experiment [195] at 10.6 μm. In this experiment a 10 MW peak output power was observed with an average power of 6 kW over a 90 μsec macropulse. Subharmonic bunching was used to obtain peak currents of 40 A at an energy of 20 MeV. The output of the oscillator was very sensitive to low-frequency noise in the klystron amplifiers and electron gun.[149] This is important in nonlinear efficiency enhancement techniques, such as tapering the wiggler, where phase and amplitude control are critical.

One of the most attractive features of the free-electron laser, as compared with conventional lasers, is the ability to tune the output frequency. Figure 35 is a plot of the output wavelength versus electron beam energy for the LANL FEL oscillator experiment,[195] where the wavelength was tuned from 9 to 35 μm by varying the electron beam energy from 11.5 to 23 MeV.

Excitation of sideband radiation from the electrons trapped in the ponderomotive wave has been predicted theoretically.[43,62,63,65,69,196,197] This instability produces sidebands about the main signal resulting in a broadening of the spectrum. At LANL, Warren *et al.*[73] observed sidebands in the oscillator experiment in qualitative agreement with theory. Figure 36 shows an example of the radiation output spectrum. There is a main signal around 10.35 μm with a sideband at roughly 2% longer wavelength. By changing the cavity tuning, the evolution of the instability could be altered. Several experiments[74,196] have successfully demonstrated the reduction of sidebands using filters and cavity detuning, at the expense of reduced efficiency for uniform wigglers, but an increase in efficiency for tapered wigglers.

The LANL FEL experiment has been improved by suppressing wake fields in the wiggler region. This resulted in a higher beam current (350 A) capability, increasing the FEL efficiency to 4.4% at 10.6 μm. The stored power level was sufficiently high that two synchrotron oscillations occurred in the length of the wiggler, without the appearance of sidebands.[101]

Benson *et al.*[158,198] have reported operation of a FEL oscillator in the 3.1–2.6 μm range using a single section of the Stanford Mark III rf linac and a microwave gun injector. The gain per pass was 28% and the macropulse was 2.5 μsec long. Micropulses with peak powers as high as 2 MW and micropulse lengths as short as 0.5 psec were observed during

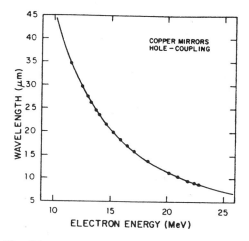

Fig. 35 — Continuous wavelength range (9-35 μm)
in the LANL FEL oscillator

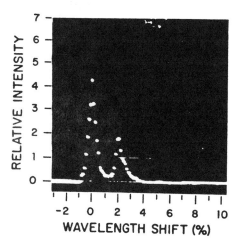

Fig. 36 — Relative intensity versus wavelength shift, from 10.35 μm
showing the growth of a side band in the LANL oscillator

the 2.5 μsec macropulse. Also coherent radiation at the fifth and seventh harmonics was observed.

LaSala *et al.*[100] have reported measurements of optical guiding using the Stanford Mark III rf linac. Radiation was coupled out of the FEL cavity and focused onto sampling apertures. The ratios of the radiation intensity on axis to off axis were measured and compared with simulation. It was found that the intracavity transverse mode was smaller than the diffraction limited mode as a result of strong optical guiding in the small-signal regime but grew larger after saturation as a result of reduced gain. The experiment indicated that in the saturated regime refractive guiding dominated over gain focusing.

Smith[199] examined the problem of preserving the brightness of a beam as it is transported through a rf linac accelerator. In particular, rf phase effects degrade the brightness because different electrons experience different rf phases as they pass through the cavity. He carried out calculations to include harmonics of the accelerating field. Harmonic contributions to the accelerating field can produce a "flattop" pulse, thereby reducing the degradation in the beam quality during acceleration.

The Boeing Aerospace Company, teamed with Los Alamos National Laboratory, has been carrying out a series of major projects aimed at a high power oscillator demonstration. For this purpose a new 1.3 GHz rf linac at Boeing has been constructed. The linac is designed to produce a 120 MeV electron beam with peak current up to 300 A in 16 psec micropulses.[200] The macropulse is 80 μsec long and can be extended to 200 μsec, with average currents up to 100 mA. Specifications call for a flatness < 1% during each 80 μsec pulse. In order to achieve high-brightness beams, an injector system which includes a SLAC-type 100 kV gun, two subharmonic prebunchers, and a high power tapered-phase-velocity buncher was built. The beam emerges from the injector system at 2 MeV, sufficiently relativistic that space-charge effects are small through the remainder of the linac.

The Boeing Aerospace group measured the normalized edge emittance at the linac exit to be about 50 mm mrad, the lowest achieved anywhere for such beam currents. In preliminary experiments, one percent of the beam was converted into visible light at 0.6 μm. The power in the optical oscillator was 40 MW peak and 2 kW average.[201] This is the highest power achieved to date at visible wavelengths.

At Bell Laboratories[202] a microtron accelerator is being used to drive a FEL in the infrared regime ($\sim 100 \mu m$). The microtron beam consists of 18 μsec long pulses at 18 MeV, with an average current of 50 mA. The short radiation pulses from this FEL have many applications in condensed-matter studies.[203] A microtron driven 100 μm wavelength Čerenkov FEL experiment has been performed by Walsh et al.[204] at Dartmouth College.

D. Free-electron lasers driven by electrostatic accelerators

Elias et al. have carried out FEL experiments at UCSB using a van de Graaf electrostatic accelerator.[102,150] Electrostatic accelerators produce high quality electron beams because of the homogeneous accelerating electric fields. Hence the transverse beam emittance is not degraded by the accelerating structure, as is the case in rf accelerators. An additional advantage of electrostatic accelerators is that the pulse length can be varied from microseconds to DC. However,

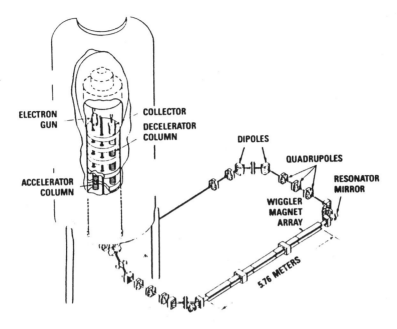

Fig. 37 — Sketch of the UCSB electrostatic accelerator

they are limited to low current operation. To overcome this limitation, the beam can be decelerated, collected, and recirculated through the wiggler. In this way the charging current need only equal the current lost in the recovery process. In addition to providing higher beam currents, recirculation enhances the overall efficiency and results in lower radiation shielding requirements.

A sketch of the UCSB FEL experiment[150] is shown in Fig. 37. The 10 m vertical-standing high pressure tank houses two accelerator tubes. A high-voltage terminal surrounded by an equipotential metallic shell contains an electron gun, electron collector, and a pelletron high-voltage

123

charging system. The electron beam transport system consists of 10 bending magnets, 17 quadrupole magnets, and 24 steering coils.

The present UCSB FEL accelerator operates with a beam voltage between 2 and 6 MeV, and a current of 2.6 A. The FEL generates 10 kW of radiation between 400 μm and 100 μm, and fractional line widths of 10^{-8} have been reported.[102]

The voltage of an electrostatic accelerator is typically limited to less than 30 MeV. To overcome this voltage limitation the UCSB group is investigating a two-stage FEL,[205] and microwigglers.[206] The program is designed to operate as a user's facility and provide tunable, high power radiation in the relatively unexplored far infrared portion of the spectrum. This computer controlled FEL provides ease of operation by the user from the work station.

E. Free-electron lasers driven by storage rings

The first operation of a FEL in the visible regime was achieved using the ACO storage ring at Orsay, France. The results of these experiments have been reviewed by Billardon et al.[207,208] The storage ring is generally operated at energies of 160–224 MeV and currents of 16–100 mA with a lifetime of 60–90 min. The maximum average power, which was determined directly, was 50 mW, with less than 1 mW extracted. In addition, the experiments verified Renieri's limit.[209] This limit states that the maximum FEL output power is proportional to the product of total synchrotron power emitted in the ring, and the fractional energy spread of the beam.

The experiments demonstrated that the laser power was proportional to the ring current and the fourth power of the beam energy.

The laser operated at three wavelengths; the dominant wavelength was 6476 Å. Figure 38 shows the spectra with the optical cavity both tuned and detuned. The spontaneous spectrum contained all harmonics of the fundamental wavelength. Intense emission was observed for the first 20 harmonics and a spectral brilliance at 300 Å was 300 times brighter than the classical synchrotron. The ACO storage ring FEL was also operated in an optical klystron mode.

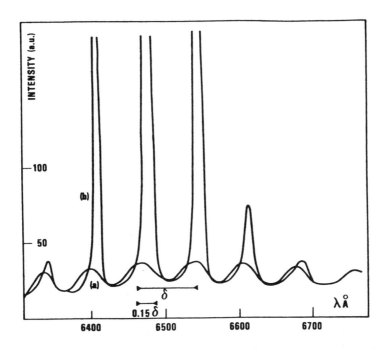

Fig. 38 — Spectra of the output from the Orsay storage ring FEL. The laser operated at three wavelengths. The dominant wavelength was 6470 Å.

Although the lifetime of the electron ring is more than an hour, the ring does not emit radiation in a steady-state mode, but it exhibits a noisy pulsed microtemporal structure. However, high power pulsed Q-switched operation was possible by a small variation in rf frequency or a small deflection of the electron beam. The result was stable periodic laser operation with no decrease in average power, but several orders of magnitude increase in peak power.

Since the optical gain per pass was low, laser oscillation required the use of high reflectivity mirrors. Degradation of the mirrors was due to the spontaneous UV harmonic emission from the wiggler. Mirror degradation is expected to be a critical problem for future UV and XUV free-electron laser oscillators.

In going through the spectrum from the microwave to the XUV region, the most significant difference is the reduced gain per pass. Since the gain decreases with wavelength this requires higher mirror reflectivities and higher beam quality. Because of the limited performance of short wavelength optics, an XUV FEL must operate in the high-gain Compton regime.[37,210] In addition to operation in the high-gain regime, self-focusing, or optical guiding may be required to increase the gain as well.[54,211] Figure 39 is a plot of gain versus optical wavelength of the storage ring FEL.[212] The solid curves represent single pass gain for three different wiggler periods determined from a computer simulation. The empty circles are the calculated gain assuming free space propagation. The presence of optical guiding results in significantly higher gain for all but the shortest wavelengths considered, where diffraction is less important.

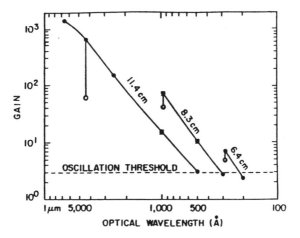

Fig. 39 — Calculation of gain vs optical wavelength for a storage ring
with optical guiding (squares) and without optical guiding (circles)

VIII. WIGGLERS AND RESONATORS

The earliest FEL experiments at Stanford University
employed electromagnets with the coils wound in order to
generate a helical magnetic wiggler field.[10,11] On the axis,
such a field may be represented by Eq. (1). Since the early
experiments there has been substantial progress in the design[213] and fabrication of wigglers and a shift toward the use
of planar wigglers.[104] Near the axis, the planar wiggler field
may be represented by $B_w = B_w \sin(k_w z)\hat{e}_y$. The preference
for planar wigglers is mainly due to the greater ease in con-
struction and in the greater accessibility to the vacuum
chamber. However, when an axial guide field is employed
the electron beam may be significantly distorted unless focusing symmetry is maintained.[214,215]

Defining the dimensionless wiggler parameter as a_w $= |e|B_w /k_w m_0 c^2$, and the wiggler period as $\lambda_w = 2\pi/k_w$, the radiation wavelength is given by $\lambda = \lambda_w (1 + a_w^2)/(2\gamma_0^2)$ for a helical wiggler field. For a planar wiggler field, a_w^2 is replaced with $a_w^2/2$.

The gain and efficiency of a FEL is an increasing function of a_w. In addition, larger values of a_w provide a larger tunability range (for a given beam energy), and larger harmonic-radiation gains. Thus it is desirable to increase the wiggler field strength. To achieve higher field strengths the ampere turns per coil must be increased. The requirement for higher coil current densities, particularly at shorter wavelengths, necessitates the use of superconducting coils. This problem has led to the development of permanent magnets for use in FEL's. Rare-earth cobalt (REC) permanent magnets are now in use in many laboratories throughout the world. These materials provide high magnetic fields, ~ 10 kG, for FEL research and for insertion devices for synchrotron radiation sources.[216,217]

In the design of wigglers it is common to join small blocks of REC magnets with different directions of magnetization to obtain the desired field pattern. For a simple design with four blocks per period the magnitude of the field on axis[104] is $B_w = 1.4B_r \exp(-\pi g/\lambda_w)$, where B_r is the remnant magnetic field (~ 8–10 kG) and g is the gap spacing. This formula expresses the essential scaling of the gap spacing with the wiggler period λ_w.

The inevitable variation of the strength and the direction of magnetization from block to block in pure REC designs has an adverse effect on the distribution of the magnetic field and thus the electron beam trajectory. As a result hybrid designs making use of steel poles in conjunction with

128

REC material are being developed. Hybrid designs offer the advantages of larger fields and diminished sensitivity to variations in the magnetization of REC blocks.

To enhance FEL efficiency, variable parameter or tapered wigglers can be used where the period and/or the field strength is profiled to match the desired decrease in electron energy. The use of permanent magnets is ideal for this purpose. In the optical klystron, extraction is improved by making use of two wigglers separated by a drift section. This design increases the degree of bunching of the electrons and hence the gain. The concept of the optical klystron was first developed by Vinokurov and Skrinskii at Novosibirsk[218] and its use was critical to the successful operation of the first visible FEL on the ACO storage ring in Orsay University.[103]

Lasers in general may be designed to operate in two different modes: as oscillators or as amplifiers. In the latter, an input signal enters the device at one end, interacts with the active medium, and is amplified as it makes a single pass through the device. Amplifiers, therefore, are useful for the purposes of amplifying a weak input signal, so that the output may then be detected (demodulated) or used to drive the next stage. In an oscillator, on the other hand, there is no input signal as such; rather, it is the spontaneous noise present in the active medium that is amplified by the lasing action. Since the level of the spontaneous radiation is generally very small, a single pass through the device is insufficient to produce a detectable output. For this reason the lasing medium is generally placed inside a resonant cavity. As a result the radiation field is reflected back and forth inside the cavity, the net amplification after many passes being such that a useful amount of radiation may be extracted from the laser.[122]

Optical resonators may be divided into two groups, stable or unstable. The distinction arises because, with proper choice of the separation and curvature of the mirrors, it is possible for a ray of light to gradually "walk out" of the resonator after many bounces between the mirrors. This is an example of an unstable cavity. Stable cavities are generally preferred, especially for low power lasers.

An important figure of merit for the mirrors comprising a resonator is referred to as the Fresnel number $N \equiv a^2/\lambda d$, where a is the mirror radius, d is the intramirror separation, and λ is the radiation wavelength. The larger the Fresnel number, the smaller the diffractive losses of the radiation at the edges of the mirror. For $N \lesssim 1$, the radiation in a cavity tends to be concentrated in the lowest-order Gaussian mode. The reason for this is that the higher-order modes have relatively larger amplitudes off axis, and therefore suffer a greater loss on each reflection from the mirror surface. For high power operation, however, a large active volume and therefore a high Fresnel number resonator is required. Since it is difficult to arrange for single-mode oscillation in a large-N stable cavity, the use of unstable cavities has become common for these purposes. Although such cavities have much higher losses, this shortcoming is largely compensated by the larger mode volume and an efficient diffraction coupling that eliminates the shortcomings of partially transmitting mirrors.[105,122]

The development of suitable mirrors is a key issue for developing tunable high power FEL's at short wavelengths. For example, the Boeing Aerospace high power FEL experiments require a sophisticated ring resonator. The ring resonator features hyperboloid mirrors set at 3° to the FEL axis, 50 m apart, to avoid optical damage. Two paraboloids and

130

two flat mirrors complete the resonator design. One of the flats includes provision for 20% outcoupling and the other is designed for on-line, dynamic stabilization. The 5 m long wiggler includes provision for tapering the magnetic field up to 12%, and employs an unusually strong, 10 kG field. The Boeing Aerospace facility should provide a test bed for studying a number of important issues, including harmonic content, optical guiding effects, pulse stability, and side-bands, all at visible wavelengths.

IX. DISCUSSION

The FEL is rapidly becoming a practical source of tunable coherent radiation. Electron beam quality is a major limiting factor in extending FEL's to higher power and shorter wavelengths. This has led to a strong interest in producing electron sources with high current density and small energy spreads. In the past decade a variety of wiggler configurations have led to novel and compact FEL configurations. The development of suitable mirrors is another key issue for tunable high power sources at short wavelengths. Optical guiding provides a means of overcoming the limited interaction length at short wavelengths. The nonlinear dynamics of the interaction continues to be an important theoretical problem. An order-of-magnitude improvement in experimental extraction efficiency has been achieved using designs based on these nonlinear calculations.

The demand for high power microwave radiation has led to several new sources at long wavelengths.[219] These devices often employ electron beams of sufficient intensity where the Debye length is short compared to the radius. In this case the beam constitutes a nonneutral plasma.[220] Trapping and cooling experiments with electrons and positrons have led to the possibility of new cryogenic sources for accelerators.[221]

A number of variations on the FEL concept have also been suggested. These ideas include prebunching the electron beam prior to entering the wiggler,[222] gas loaded FEL's,[223] compact cyclic FEL's,[224] sheet electron beams with small period wigglers,[225] and the use of crystalline fields for generation of short wavelength radiation.[226,227]

The FEL has been the subject of intense international research. The results of this research have indicated that it will represent an important addition to the collection of coherent radiation devices.

ACKNOWLEDGMENTS

The authors are extremely grateful and indebted to B. Hafizi for his many helpful discussions and recommendations concerning this review paper. We also want to thank C. M. Tang, H. Freund, Y. Y. Lau, and T. Godlove for their many useful comments. Finally, we wish to acknowledge the excellent work of Bertha Pitcher, Wilma Brizzi, and Ruth Bain.

This work was supported by the Office of Naval Research (ONR).

REFERENCES

[1]T. C. Marshall, *Free Electron Lasers* (Macmillan, New York, 1985), p. 78.
[2]P. Sprangle and T. Coffey, Phys. Today 37, 44 (1984).

[3] *Free Electron Generation of Extreme Ultraviolet Coherent Radiation*, AIP Conference Proceedings No. 118, edited by J. M. J. Madey and C. Pellegrini (American Institute of Physics, New York, 1984).

[4] *Free Electron Laser Handbook*, edited by W. Colson, C. Pellegrini, and A. Renieri (North-Holland, Amsterdam, in press).

[5] H. Motz, J. Appl. Phys. **22**, 527 (1951).

[6] H. Motz, Contemp. Phys. **20**, 547 (1979).

[7] R. M. Phillips, IRE Trans. Electron Devices ED-7, 231 (1960).

[8] R. M. Phillips, Nucl. Instrum. Methods A **271**, 1 (1988).

[9] J. M. J. Madey, J. Appl. Phys. **42**, 1906 (1971).

[10] L. R. Elias, W. M. Fairbanks, J. M. J. Madey, H. A. Schwettman, and T. I. Smith, Phys. Rev. Lett. **36**, 717 (1976).

[11] D. A. G. Deacon, L. R. Elias, J. M. J. Madey, G. J. Ramian, H. A. Schwettman, and T. I. Smith, Phys. Rev. Lett. **38**, 892 (1977).

[12] R. J. Briggs, *Electronic Stream Interaction with Plasmas* (MIT Press, Cambridge, MA, 1964).

[13] W. E. Drummond and D. Pines, Nucl. Fusion Suppl., Part 3, 1049 (1963).

[14] A. A. Vedenov, E. P. Velikhov, and R. Z. Sagdeev, Nucl. Fusion **1**, 82 (1961).

[15] W. E. Drummond, J. H. Malmberg, T. M. O'Neil, and J. R. Thompson, Phys. Fluids **13**, 2422 (1970).

[16] T. M. O'Neil, J. H. Winfrey, and J. H. Malmberg, Phys. Fluids **14**, 1204 (1971).

[17] J. R. Thompson, Phys. Fluids **14**, 1532 (1971).

[18] J. M. Dawson and R. Shanny, Phys. Fluids **11**, 1506 (1968).

[19] R. L. Morse and C. W. Nielsen, Phys. Fluids **12**, 2418 (1969); Phys. Rev. Lett. **23**, 1087 (1969).

[20] C. Roberson, K. W. Gentle, and P. Neilsen, Phys. Rev. Lett. **26**, 226 (1971).

[21] C. Roberson and K. W. Gentle, Phys. Fluids **14**, 2462 (1971).

[22] K. W. Gentle and C. W. Roberson, Phys. Fluids **14**, 2789 (1971).

[23] K. W. Gentle and J. Lohr, Phys. Fluids **16**, 1464 (1973).

[24] R. B. Miller, *An Introduction to the Physics of Intense Charged Particle Beams* (Plenum, New York, 1982), p. 180.

[25] D. C. Forster, Adv. Microwaves 3, 301 (1968).

[26] A. Staprans, E. W. McCume, and J. A. Ruetz, Proc. IEEE **61**, 299 (1973).

[27] J. A. Nation, Appl. Phys. Lett. **17**, 491 (1970).

[28] M. Friedman and M. Herndon, Phys. Rev. Lett. **28**, 210 (1972).

[29]P. Sprangle, J. Plasma Phys. **11**, 299 (1974).

[30]P. Sprangle and V. L. Granatstein, Appl. Phys. Lett. **25**, 377 (1974).

[31]W. B. Colson, Phys. Lett. A **64**, 190 (1977).

[32]A. A. Kolomenskii and A. N. Lebedev, Sov. J. Quantum Electron. **8**, 879 (1978).

[33]N. M. Kroll and W. A. McMullin, Phys. Rev. A **17**, 300 (1978).

[34]J. M. J. Madey, Nuovo Cimento B **50**, 64 (1970).

[35]A. Hasegawa, Bell Syst. Tech. J. **57**, 3069 (1978).

[36]P. Sprangle and A. T. Drobot, J. Appl. Phys. **50**, 2652 (1979).

[37]P. Sprangle and R. A. Smith, Phys. Rev. A **21**, 293 (1980); P. Sprangle, R. A. Smith, and V. L. Granatstein, in *Infrared and Millimeter Waves*, edited by K. J. Button (Academic, New York, 1979), Vol. 1, p. 279.

[38]A. Nordsieck, Proc. IRE **41**, 630 (1953).

[39]P. Sprangle, C. M. Tang, and W. M. Manheimer, Phys. Rev. Lett. **43**, 1932 (1979); Phys. Rev. A **21**, 302 (1980).

[40]P. Sprangle, C. M. Tang, and W. M. Manheimer, in *Free Electron Generators of Coherent Radiation, Physics of Quantum Electronics*, edited by S. Jacobs, H. Pilloff, M. Sargent, M. Scully, and R. Spitzer (Addison–Wesley, Reading, MA, 1980), Vol. 7, Chap. 21, p. 571.

[41]A. T. Lin and J. M. Dawson, Phys. Rev. Lett. **42**, 1670 (1979).

[42]N. M. Kroll, P. L. Morton, and N. M. Rosenbluth, in Ref. 40, Chap. 5, p. 113.

[43]N. M. Kroll, P. L. Morton, and M. N. Rosenbluth, IEEE J. Quantum Electron. **QE-17**, 1436 (1981).

[44]A. Szoke, V. K. Neil, and D. Prosnitz, in Ref. 40, Chap. 7, p. 175.

[45]D. Prosnitz, A. Szoke, and V. R. Neil, Phys. Rev. A **24**, 1436 (1981).

[46]C. A. Brau and R. K. Cooper, in Ref. 40, Chap. 24, p. 647.

[47]C. M. Tang and P. Sprangle, J. Appl. Phys. **52**, 3148 (1981).

[48]A. T. Lin, Phys. Fluids **24**, 316 (1981).

[49]G. J. Morales, Phys. Fluids **23**, 2472 (1980).

[50]S. I. Tsunoda and J. H. Malmberg, Phys. Fluids **27**, 2557 (1984).

[51]M. N. Rosenbluth, B. N. Moore, and H. V. Wong, IEEE J. Quantum Electron. **QE-21**, 1026 (1985).

[52]W. B. Colson, Nucl. Instrum. Methods A **237**, 1 (1985).

[53]P. Sprangle, C. M. Tang, and C. W. Roberson, Nucl. Instrum. Methods, Phys. Res. A **239**, 1 (1985); *Laser Handbook*, edited by M. Stitch and M. S. Bass (North-Holland, Amsterdam, in press), Vol. 4.

[54]P. Sprangle and C. M. Tang, Appl. Phys. Lett. **39**, 677 (1981); AIAA J. **19**, 1164 (1981).

[55]G. T. Moore, Opt. Commun. **52**, 46 (1984); **54**, 121 (1985); Nucl. Instrum. Meth. Phys. Res. A **239**, 19 (1985).

[56]E. T. Scharlemann, A. M. Sessler, and J. S. Wurtele, Phys. Rev. Lett. **54**, 1925 (1985); Nucl. Instrum. Methods A **239**, 29 (1985).

[57]P. Sprangle, A. Ting, and C. M. Tang, Phys. Rev. Lett. **59**, 202 (1987); Phys. Rev. A **36**, 2773 (1987); P. Sprangle, A. Ting, B. Hafizi, and C. M. Tang, in *Proceedings of the 1987 IEEE Particle Accelerator Conference*, March 1987, Washington, DC, edited by E. R. Lindstrom and L. S. Taylor (IEEE, New York, 1987), Vol. 1, p. 189.

[58]W. B. Colson, IEEE J. Quantum Electron. **QE-17**, 1417 (1981).

[59]W. B. Colson, G. Dattoli, and F. Ciocci, Phys. Rev. A **31**, 828 (1985).

[60]D. Carlson, W. Fann, and J. M. J. Madey, Nucl. Instrum. Methods A **272**, 92 (1988).

[61]S. Penner, R. Ayres, R. Cutler, P. Debenham, B. C. Johnson, E. Lindstrom, D. Mohr, J. Rose, M. Wilson, P. Sprangle, and C. M. Tang, Nucl. Instrum. Methods A **272**, 73 (1988).

[62]N. M. Kroll and M. N. Rosenbluth, in Ref. 40, p. 147.

[63]W. B. Colson and R. S. Freedman, Phys. Rev. A **27**, 1399 (1983).

[64]A. T. Lin, in *Physics of Quantum Electronics*, edited by S. F. Jacobs, G. T. Moore, H. S. Pillof, M. Sargent III, M. O. Scully, and R. Spitzer (Addison–Wesley, Reading, MA, 1982), Vol. 9, p. 409.

[65]D. C. Quimby, J. M. Slater, and J. P. Wilcoxon, IEEE J. Quantum Electron. **QE-21**, 979 (1985).

[66]R. A. Freedman and W. B. Colson, Opt. Commun. **52**, 409 (1985).

[67]J. C. Goldstein, B. E. Newnam, and R. W. Warren, Nucl. Instrum. Methods A **272**, 150 (1988).

[68]B. Hafizi, A. Ting, P. Sprangle, and C. M. Tang, Phys. Rev. A **38**, 197 (1988).

[69]S. Riyopoulos and C. M. Tang, Phys. Fluids **31**, 1708 (1988); *ibid.* **31**, 3387 (1988).

[70]J. Masud, T. C. Marshall, F. G. Yee, and S. P. Schlesinger, Nucl. Instrum. Methods A **250**, 342 (1986).

[71]J. Masud, T. C. Marshall, S. P. Schlesinger, F. G. Yee, W. M. Fawley, E. T. Scharlemann, S. S. Yu, A. M. Sessler, and E. T. Sternbach, Phys. Rev. Lett. **58**, 763 (1987).

[72]F. G. Yee, T. C. Marshall, and S. P. Schlesinger, IEEE Trans. Plasma Sci. **PS-16**, 162 (1988).

[73]R. W. Warren, B. E. Newman, and J. C. Goldstein, IEEE J. Quantum Electron. **QE-21**, 882 (1985).

[74]R. Warren and J. C. Goldstein, Nucl. Instrum. Methods A **272**, 155 (1988).

[75]C. B. Wharton, J. H. Malmberg, and T. M. O'Neil, Phys. Fluids **11**, 1761 (1968).

[76]C. P. Deneef, J. H. Malmberg, and T. M. O'Neil, Phys. Rev. Lett. **30**, 1032 (1973).

[77]C. W. Roberson and J. Fukai, J. Appl. Phys. **45**, 2489 (1974).

[78]T. Starke and J. H. Malmberg, Phys. Rev. Lett. **37**, 505 (1976); Phys. Fluids **12**, 2242 (1978).

[79]W. L. Kruer, J. M. Dawson, and R. N. Sudan, Phys. Rev. Lett. **23**, 838 (1969).

[80]M. V. Goldman, Phys. Fluids **13**, 1281 (1970).

[81]H. V. Wong, Phys. Fluids **15**, 632 (1972).

[82]P. Sprangle, V. L. Granatstein, and L. Baker, Phys. Rev. A **12**, 1697 (1975).

[83]L. Friedland, Phys. Fluids **23**, 2376 (1980).

[84]H. P. Freund, P. Sprangle, D. Dillenburg, E. H. da Jornada, B. Liberman, and R. S. Schneider, Phys. Rev. A **24**, 1965 (1981); *ibid.* **26**, 2004 (1982).

[85]C. W. Roberson, J. Quantum Electron. **QE-21**, 860 (1985).

[86]T. M. O'Neil and J. H. Malmberg, Phys. Fluids **11**, 1754 (1968).

[87]C. W. Roberson, Y. Y. Lau, and H. P. Freund, in *High Brightness Accelerator*, The NATO Advanced Study Institute Series, edited by A. K. Hyder, M. F. Rose, and A. H. Guenther (Plenum, New York, 1988), Vol. 187, p. 627.

[88]G. Saxon, Nucl. Instrum. Methods A **37**, 309 (1985).

[89]R. K. Cooper, P. L. Morton, P. B. Wilson, D. Keefe, and A. Faltens, J. Phys. (Paris) **44**, C1-185 (1983).

[90]R. J. Briggs, D. L. Birx, D. S. Prono, D. Prosnitz, and L. L. Regimato, in *Proceedings of the 1987 IEEE Particle Accelerator Conference*, March 1987, Washington, DC, edited by E. R. Lindstrom and L. S. Taylor (IEEE, New York, 1987), p. 178.

[91]S. Penner, in Ref. 90, p. 183.

[92]R. K. Parker, R. H. Jackson, S. H. Gold, H. P. Freund, V. L. Granatstein, P. C. Efthimion, M. Herndon, and H. K. Kinkead, Phys. Rev. Lett. **48**, 238 (1982).

[93]S. C. Chen and T. C. Marshall, Phys. Rev. Lett. **52**, 425 (1984); J. Quantum Electron. **QE-21**, 924 (1985).

[94]S. Y. Cai, A. Bhattacharjee, and T. C. Marshall, IEEE J. Quantum Electron. **QE-23**, 1651 (1987).

[95]J. Fajans, G. Bekefi, Y. Z. Yin, and B. Lax, Phys. Fluids **28**, 1995 (1985).

[96]C. W. Roberson, J. A. Pasour, F. Mako, R. F. Lucey, and P. Sprangle, Infrared Millimeter Waves **10**, 361 (1983).

[97]J. A. Pasour and S. Gold, IEEE J. Quantum Electron. **QE-21**, 845 (1985).

[98]T. J. Orzechowski, E. T. Scharlemann, B. Anderson, V. K. Neil, W. M. Fawley, D. Prosnitz, S. M. Yarema, D. B. Hopkins, A. C. Paul, A. M. Sessler, and J. S. Wurtele, IEEE J. Quantum Electron. **QE-21**, 831 (1985).

[99]T. J. Orzechowski, B. R. Anderson, J. C. Clark, W. M. Fawley, A. C. Paul, D. Prosnitz, E. T. Scharlemann, S. M. Yarema, D. B. Hopkins, A. M. Sessler, and J. S. Wurtele, Phys. Rev. Lett. **57**, 17 (1986).

[100]J. E. La Sala, D. A. G. Deacon, and J. M. J. Madey, Phys. Rev. Lett. **59**, 2047 (1988).

[101]R. W. Warren (private communication); Nucl. Instrum. Methods (in press).

[102]L. R. Elias, G. Ramian, J. Hu, and A. Amir, Phys. Rev. Lett. **57**, 424 (1986).

[103]M. Billardon, P. Elleaume, J. M. Ortega, C. Bazin, M. Bergher, M. Velghe, Y. Petroff, D. A. G. Deacon, K. E. Robinson, and J. M. J. Madey, Phys. Rev. Lett. **51**, 1652 (1983).

[104]R. P. Walker, Nucl. Instrum. Methods A **237**, 366 (1985).

[105]S. Solimono and A. Torre, Nucl. Instrum. Methods A **237**, 404 (1985).

[106]*Free Electron Lasers*, Proceedings of the 1984 Free Electron Laser Conference, Castelgandolfo (Rome), Italy, September, 1984, edited by J. M. J. Madey and A. Renieri (North-Holland, Amsterdam, 1985).

[107]*Free Electron Lasers*, Proceedings of the Seventh International Conference on Free Electron Lasers, Tahoe City, California, September, 1985, edited by E. T. Scharlemann and D. Prosnitz (North-Holland, Amsterdam, 1986).

[108]*Free Electron Lasers*, Proceedings of the Eighth International Free Electron Laser Conference, Glasgow, United Kingdom, September, 1986, edited by M. Poole (North-Holland, Amsterdam, 1986).

[109]*Free Electron Lasers*, Proceedings of the Ninth International Free Electron Laser Conference, Williamsburg, VA, September 1987, edited by P. Sprangle, J. Walsh, and C. M. Tang (North-Holland, Amsterdam, 1988).

[110]A. Szoke, editor, *Special Issue on Free-Electron Lasers*, IEEE J. Quantum Electron. **QE-17**, 1326 (1981).

[111]L. R. Elias and W. B. Colson, editors, *Special Issue on Free-Electron Lasers*, IEEE J. Quantum Electron. **QE-19**, 256 (1983).

[112]V. L. Granatstein and C. W. Roberson, editors, *Special Issue on Free-Electron Lasers*, IEEE J. Quantum Electron. **QE-21**, 804 (1985).

[113]C. A. Brau and B. E. Newnam, editors, *Special Issue on Free-Electron Lasers*, IEEE J. Quantum Electron. **QE-23**, 1468 (1987).

[114]P. Diament, Phys. Rev. A **23**, 2537 (1981); J. Fajans, D. A. Kirkpatrick, and G. Bekefi, Phys. Rev. A **32**, 3448 (1985).

[115]A. M. Dimos and R. C. Davidson, Phys. Fluids **28**, 677 (1985).

[116]C. M. Tang and P. Sprangle, J. Appl. Phys. **53**, 831 (1982).

[117]T. Kwan, J. M. Dawson, and A. T. Lin, Phys. Fluids **20**, 581 (1977).

[118]M. N. Rosenbluth, H. V. Wong, and B. N. Moore, in *Free-Electron Generators of Coherent Radiation*, edited by C. A. Brau, S. F. Jacobs, and M. O. Scully (SPIE, Bellingham, WA, 1983), Vol. 453, p. 25.

[119]B. Hafizi, P. Sprangle, and A. Ting, Phys. Rev. A **36**, 1739 (1987).

[120]M. Xie and A. G. Deacon, Nucl. Instrum. Methods A **250**, 426 (1986).

[121]T. M. Antonsen and B. Levush, Nucl. Instrum. Methods A **272**, 472 (1988).

[122]A. E. Siegman, *An Introduction to Lasers and Masers* (McGraw-Hill, New York, 1971), Chap. 8; A. Yariv, *Quantum Electronics* (Wiley, New York, 1975), Chap. 6.

[123]E. T. Scharlemann, J. Appl. Phys. **58**, 2154 (1985).

[124]H. P. Freund and P. Sprangle, Phys. Rev. A **28**, 1835 (1983).

[125]I. B. Bernstein and J. L. Hirshfield, Phys. Rev. A **20**, 1661 (1979).

[126]I. B. Bernstein and L. Friedland, Phys. Rev. A **23**, 816 (1981).

[127]R. C. Davidson and H. S. Uhm, Phys. Fluids **23**, 2076 (1980); J. Appl. Phys. **53**, 2910 (1982).

[128]L. Friedland and J. L. Hirshfield, Phys. Rev. Lett. **44**, 1456 (1980).

[129]L. F. Ibanez and S. Johnston, IEEE J. Quantum Electron. **QE-19**, 339 (1983).

[130]H. P. Freund and A. K. Ganguly, Phys. Rev. A **28**, 3438 (1983).

[131]H. P. Freund and A. K. Ganguly, Phys. Rev. A **33**, 1060 (1985); *ibid.* **34**, 1242 (1986); IEEE J. Quantum Electron. **QE-23**, 1657 (1987).

[132]A. K. Ganguly and H. P. Freund, Phys. Rev. A **32**, 2275 (1985); IEEE Trans. Plasma Sci. **PS-16**, 167 (1988).

[133]E. P. Lee and R. K. Cooper, Part. Accel. **7**, 83 (1976).

[134]J. D. Lawson, *The Physics of Charged Particle Beams* (Oxford U.P., London, 1977).

[135]T. I. Smith and J. M. J. Madey, Appl. Phys. B **27**, 195 (1982).

[136]V. K. Neil (private communication).

[137]G. Dattoli, T. Letardi, J. M. J. Madey, and A. Renieri, in Ref. 118, pp. 189–195.

[138]C. W. Roberson, in Ref. 118, Vol. 453, p. 320.

[139]J. D. Lawson and S. Penner, IEEE J. Quantum Electron. **QE-21**, 174 (1985).

[140]W. A. Barletta, J. K. Boyd, A. C. Paul, and D. S. Prono, Nucl. Instrum. Methods A **37**, 318 (1985).

[141]J. S. Fraser and R. L. Sheffield, IEEE J. Quantum Electron. QE-23, 1489 (1987); J. S. Fraser, R. L. Sheffield, E. R. Gray, P. M. Giles, R. W. Springer, and V. A. Loebs, in *IEEE Particle Accelerator Conference* (IEEE, New York, 1987), p. 1705.

[142]Y. Y. Lau, J. Appl. Phys. 61, 36 (1987).

[143]J. R. Thompson (private communication).

[144]J. A. Pasour, R. F. Lucey, and C. W. Roberson, in *Free-Electron Generators of Coherent Radiation*, edited by C. A. Brau, S. F. Jacobs, and M. O. Scully, (SPIE, Bellingham, 1984), Vol. 453, p. 328.

[145]R. Prohaska and A. Fisher, Rev. Sci. Instrum. 53, 1092 (1982).

[146]J. J. Ramirez and D. L. Cook, J. Appl. Phys. 51, 4602 (1980).

[147]G. Bekefi, R. E. Shefer, and S. C. Tasker, Nucl. Instrum. Methods A 250, 91 (1986).

[148]G. Bekefi, F. Hartemann, and D. A. Kirkpatrick, J. Appl. Phys. 62, 1564 (1987).

[149]M. T. Lynch, R. W. Warren, and P. J. Tallerico, IEEE J. Quantum Electron. QE-21, 904 (1985).

[150]L. R. Elias, J. Hu, and G. Ramian, Nucl. Instrum. Methods A 237, 203 (1985).

[151]S. Humphries, S. Coffey, M. Savage, L. K. Len, G. W. Cooper, and D. M. Woodall, J. Appl. Phys. 57, 709 (1985).

[152]M. E. Hernitor and W. Getty, in *1987 IEEE Particle Accelerator Conference* (IEEE, New York, 1987), p. 292; IEEE Trans. Plasma Sci. PS-15, 351 (1987).

[153]P. Loschialpo and C. A. Kapetanakos, J. Appl. Phys. 63, 2552 (1988).

[154]P. E. Oettinger, in *Proceedings of the SPIE International Symposium on Fiber Optics, Opto Electronics, and Laser Applications in Science and Engineering*, Boston, MA, September 1988 (SPIE, Bellingham, WA, in press).

[155]H. Ahmed and A. N. Broers, J. Appl. Phys. 43, 2185 (1982).

[156]P. E. Oettinger, I. Bursuc, R. E. Shefer, and E. Pugh, in *Proceedings of the IEEE Particle Accelerator Conference* (IEEE, New York, 1987), p. 286.

[157]G. A. Westenskow and J. M. J. Madey, Lasers Part. Beams 2, 223 (1984).

[158]S. V. Benson and J. M. J. Madey, Lasers Part. Beams 2, 223 (1984); Nucl. Instrum. Methods A 32, 55 (1984).

[159]J. M. Buzzi, in *Fifth International Conference on High-Power Particle Beams*, edited by R. I. Briggs and A. J. Toepfer (LLNL, Livermore, CA, 1983), p. 543.

[160]P. C. Efthimion and S. P. Schlesinger, Phys. Rev. A 16, 633 (1977).

[161]T. C. Marshall, S. Talmadge, and P. Efthimion, Appl. Phys. Lett. **31**, 302 (1977).

[162]R. M. Gilgenbach, T. C. Marshall, and S. P. Schlesinger, Phys. Fluids **22**, 971 (1979).

[163]D. B. McDermott, T. C. Marshall, R. K. Parker, and V. L. Granatstein, Phys. Rev. Lett. **41**, 1368 (1978).

[164]P. Avivi, F. Dothan, A. Fruchtman, A. Ljudmirsky, and J. L. Hirshfield, Int. J. Infrared Millimeter Waves **2**, 1071 (1981).

[165]R. H. Jackson, S. H. Gold, R. K. Parker, H. P. Freund, P. C. Efthimion, V. C. Granatstein, M. Herndon, A. K. Kinkead, J. E. Kosakowski, and T. J. T. Kwan, IEEE J. Quantum Electron. **QE-19**, 346 (1983).

[166]S. H. Gold, W. M. Black, V. L. Granatstein, and A. K. Kinkead, Appl. Phys. Lett. **43**, 922 (1983).

[167]S. H. Gold, W. M. Black, H. P. Freund, V. L. Granatstein, and A. K. Kinkead, Phys. Fluids **27**, 746 (1984).

[168]F. Mako, J. A. Pasour, C. W. Roberson, and R. Lucey, Rev. Sci. Instrum. **55**, 712 (1984).

[169]S. H. Gold, D. L. Hardesty, A. K. Kinkead, L. R. Barnett, and V. L. Granatstein, Phys. Rev. Lett. **52**, 1218 (1984).

[170]K. L. Felch, I. Vallier, J. M. Buzzi, P. Drossart, H. Boehmer, H. J. Doucet, B. Eflicher, H. Lamain, and C. Rouille, IEEE J. Quantum Electron. **QE-17**, 1354 (1981).

[171]J. M. Hartemann and F. Buzzi, Nucl. Instrum. Methods (in press).

[172]R. E. Shefer and G. Bekefi, Int. J. Electron. **51**, 569 (1981).

[173]J. Fajans, J. S. Wurtele, G. Bekefi, D. S. Knowles, and K. Xu, Phys. Rev. Lett. **57**, 579 (1986); J. Fajans and G. Bekefi, Phys. Fluids **29**, 3461 (1986); T. J. Orzechowski, E. T. Scharlemann, and D. B. Hopkins, Phys. Rev. A **35**, 2184 (1987).

[174]Y. Carmel, V. L. Granatstein, and A. Gover, Phys. Rev. Lett. **51**, 566 (1983).

[175]B. G. Danly, G. Bekefi, R. C. Davidson, R. J. Temkin, T. M. Tran, and J. S. Wurtele, IEEE J. Quantum Electron. **QE-23**, 103 (1987).

[176]J. E. Leiss, N. Norris, and M. A. Wilson, Part. Accel. **10**, 223 (1980).

[177]J. R. Thompson, B. N. Moore, M. L. Sloan, and J. R. Uglum, Bull. Am. Phys. Soc. **27**, 1011 (1982).

[178]J. A. Pasour, R. F. Lucey, and C. A. Kapetanakos, Phys. Rev. Lett. **53**, 1728 (1984).

[179]N. C. Christofilos, R. E. Hester, W. A. S. Lamb, D. D. Reagan, W. A. Sherwood, and R. E. Wright, Rev. Sci. Instrum. **35**, 886 (1964).

[196]J. C. Goldstein and W. B. Colson, in *Proceedings of the International Conference in Lasers '82*, New Orleans, LA, 1982, edited by R. C. Powell (STS, McLean, VA, 1984), p. 218.

[197]R. C. Davidson and J. S. Wurtele, Phys. Fluids 30, 2825 (1987).

[198]S. V. Benson, J. Schultz, B. A. Hooper, R. Crane, and J. M. J. Madey, Nucl. Instrum. Methods A 272, 22 (1988).

[199]T. I. Smith, Nucl. Instrum. Methods A 250, 64 (1986).

[200]J. L. Adamski, W. J. Gallagher, R. C. Kennedy, B. Robinson, D. R. Shoffstall, E. L. Tyson, A. M. Vetter, and A. D. Yeremian, IEEE Trans. Nucl. Sci. NS-32, 3397 (1985).

[201]T. W. Meyer, R. L. Gullickson, B. J. Pierce, and D. R. Ponikvar, Nucl. Instrum. Methods (in press).

[202]E. D. Shaw (private communication)

[203]E. D. Shaw and C. K. N. Patel, in *Proceedings of the International Conference on Lasers '80* (STS, McLean, VA, 1981), p. 53.

[204]J. Walsh, C. Shaughnessy, R. Layman, G. Dattoli, G. P. Gallerano, and A. Renieri, Nucl. Instrum. Methods A 272, 132 (1988).

[205]L. R. Elias, Phys. Rev. Lett. 42, 977 (1979).

[206]G. Ramian, L. Elias, and I. Kimel, Nucl. Instrum. Methods A 272, 125 (1988).

[207]M. Billardon, P. Élleaume, J. M. Ortega, C. Bazin, M. Bergher, M. Velghe, D. A. G. Deacon, and Y. Petroff, J. Quantum Electron. QE-21, 805 (1985).

[208]M. Billardon, P. Elleaume, J. M. Ortega, C. Bazin, M. Bergher, M. E. Couprie, Y. Lapierre, Y. Petroff, R. Prazeres, and M. Velghe, Nucl. Instrum. Methods A 259, 72 (1987).

[209]A. Renieri, Nuovo Cimento B 53, 160 (1979).

[210]R. Bonifacio and C. Pellegrini, Opt. Commun. 50, 373 (1984).

[211]C. M. Tang and P. Sprangle, in *Free-Electron Generators of Coherent Radiation*, Physics of Quantum Electronics Series, Vol. 8, edited by S. Jacobs, G. Moore, H. Pilloff, M. Sargent, M. Scully, and R. Spitzer (Addison–Wesley, Reading, MA, 1982), p. 627.

[212]J. E. LaSala, D. A. G. Deacon, and E. T. Scharlemann, Nucl. Instrum. Methods A 250, 389 (1986).

[213]J. P. Blewett and R. Chasman, J. Appl. Phys. 48, 2692 (1977).

[214]J. A. Pasour, F. Mako, and C. W. Roberson, J. Appl. Phys. 53, 7174 (1982).

[215]B. Hafizi and R. E. Aamodt, Phys. Rev. A 29, 2656 (1984); B. Hafizi, G. L. Francis, and R. E. Aamodt, Phys. Rev. A 31, 3247 (1985).

[216]K. Halbach, IEEE Trans. Nucl. Sci. NS-26, 3882 (1979); Nucl. Instrum. Methods 169, 1 (1980); J. Phys. (Paris) 44, 211 (1983).

[180]T. J. Fessenden, D. L. Birx, R. J. Briggs, H. R. Cavagnolo, J. C. Clark, E. Cook, G. Craig, C. Hanson, R. E. Hester, E. J. Lauer, E. Moore, V. K. Neil, A. C. Paul, L. L. Reginato, D. Rogers, Jr., R. Spoerlein, and D. Trimble, in *Proceedings of the Fourth International Topical Conference on High-Power Electron and Ion Beam Research Technology*, Palaiseau, France, edited by J. H. Doucet and J. M. Buzzi (Ecole Polytechnique, Palaiseau, France, 1981), p. 813.

[181]L. L. Reginato, IEEE Trans. Nucl. Sci. NS-30, 2970 (1983).

[182]H. P. Freund, Phys. Rev. A. 37, 3371 (1988).

[183]A. L. Throop, W. M. Fawley, R. A. Jong, T. J. Orzechowski, D. Prosnitz, E. T. Scharlemann, R. D. Steven, G. A. Westenskow, D. B. Hopkins, A. M. Sessler, S. Evangelides, and K. E. Kreisher, Nucl. Instrum. Methods A 272, 12 (1988).

[184]D. Prosnitz, Bull. Am. Phys. Soc. 33, 1014 (1988).

[185]T. J. Orzechowski (private communication).

[186]K. Mima, Y. Kitagawa, T. Akiba, K. Imasaki, S. Kuruma, N. Ohigashi, S. Miyamoto, S. Fujita, S. Nakayama, Y. Tsunawaki, H. Motz, T. Taguchi, S. Nakai, and C. Yamanaka, Nucl. Instrum. Methods A 272, 106 (1988).

[187]K. Mima, K. Imasaki, S. Kurum, T. Akiba, N. Ohigashi, Y. Tsunawaki, K. Tanaka, C. Yamanaka, and S. Nakai, Nucl. Instrum. Methods (in press).

[188]T. F. Godlove (private communication).

[189]P. Sprangle, C. M. Tang, and I. B. Bernstein, Phys. Lett. 50, 1775 (1983); Phys. Rev. A 25, 2300 (1983).

[190]H. Boehmer, M. Z. Caponi, J. Edighoffer, S. Fornach, J. Munch, G. R. Neil, B. Saur, and C. Shih, Phys. Rev. Lett. 48, 141 (1982).

[191]J. Edighoffer, G. R. Neil, C. E. Hess, T. I. Smith, S. W. Fornaca, and H. A. Schwettman, Phys. Rev. Lett. 52, 344 (1984).

[192]G. R. Neil, J. A. Edighoffer, S. W. Fornaca, C. E. Hess, T. I. Smith, and H. A. Schwettman, Nucl. Instrum. Methods A 237, 199 (1985).

[193]J. A. Edighoffer, G. R. Neil, S. Fornace, H. R. Thompson, T. I. Smith, H. A. Schwettman, C. E. Hess, J. Frisch, and R. Rohatgi, Appl. Phys. Lett. 52, 1569 (1988).

[194]R. W. Warren, B. E. Newnam, J. G. Winston, W. E. Stein, L. M. Young, and C. H. Brau, IEEE J. Quantum Electron. QE-19, 391 (1983).

[195]B. E. Newnam, R. W. Warren, R. L. Sheffield, W. E. Stein, M. T. Lynch, J. S. Fraser, J. C. Goldstein, J. E. Sollid, T. A. Swann, J. M. Watson, and C. A. Brau, IEEE J. Quantum Electron. QE-21, 867 (1985).

[217]K. Halbach, J. Chin, E. Joyer, H. Winick, R. Cromi, J. Yang, and Y. Zambre, IEEE Trans. Nucl. Sci. NS-28, 3136 (1981).

[218]N. A. Vinokurov, in *Proceedings of the 10th International Conference on High Energy Charged Particle Accelerators*, Serpurkhov, USSR (MIR, Moscow, 1977), Vol. 2, p. 454.

[219]*High-Power Microwave Sources*, edited by V. Granatstein and I. Alexeff (Artech House, Boston, 1987).

[220]R. C. Davidson, *Theory of Nonneutral Plasmas* (Benjamin, Reading, MA, 1974), pp. 66–78.

[221]*Non-Neutral Plasma Physics*, edited by C. W. Roberson and C. F. Driscoll, AIP Conference Proceedings, No. 175 (American Institute of Physics, New York, 1988).

[222]D. B. McDermott, K. C. Leou, and N. C. Luhmann, Jr., Int. J. Electron. 64, 1988.

[223]A. S. Fisher, R. H. Pantell, M. B. Reid, J. Feinstein, A. H. Ho, M. Ozcan, and H. D. Dulman, Nucl. Instrum. Methods A 272, 89 (1988).

[224]G. Bekefi, R. E. Shefer, and W. W. Destler, Appl. Phys. Lett. 44, 280 (1984).

[225]V. L. Granatstein, T. M. Antonsen, Jr., J. H. Booske, W. W. Destler, P. E. Latham, B. Levush, I. D. Mayergoyz, D. J. Radack, Z. Segalov, and A. Serbeto, Nucl. Instrum. Methods A 272, 110 (1988).

[226]V. V. Beloshitskii and M. A. Kumakhov, Zh. Eksp. Teor. Fiz. 74, 1244 (1978) [Sov. Phys. JETP 47, 652 (1978)].

[227]B. Hafizi, Phys. Rev. A 30, 154 (1984); I. S. Batkin, A. N. Almaliev, and I. V. Kopytin, Zh. Tekh. Fiz. 56, 1193 (1986) [Sov. Phys. Tech. Phys. 31, 699 (1986)]; Yu. L. Pivovarov, Yu. P. Kunashenko, and S. A. Vovobiev, Radiat. Eff. 102, 117 (1987).